SWEET PEAS

SWEET PEAS

THEIR HISTORY
DEVELOPMENT CULTURE

CHARLES W. J. UNWIN, F.L.S.

FOURTH EDITION

SILENT BOOKS
CAMBRIDGE
1986

First Edition: 1926
Second Edition: 1929
Third Edition: 1952
This completely revised edition published in
Great Britain 1986 by
Silent Books, Swavesey, Cambridge CB4 5RA

ISBN 1 85183 000 6

Typeset by Goodfellow & Egan Ltd in 11/12½pt Ehrhardt
Printed and bound in Italy.

CONTENTS

DEDICATED TO MY GRANDDAUGHTER
SALLY UNWIN

PREFACE TO THE FOURTH EDITION

It is now over 30 years since the third edition of this book was published. The first three editions went out of print fairly quickly, and this, combined with many encouraging press reviews, and many appreciative letters from readers, was most gratifying. In tendering my somewhat belated, though none the less sincere thanks for this encouragement, I feel I must also warmly thank the many hundreds of Sweet Pea enthusiasts who have, since then, pressed me to write either a new Sweet Pea book, or a revised fourth edition of the old one. Circumstances have now permitted me to accede to these requests.

On reading the third edition recently I was rather surprised to realise that my opinions on cultural and most other topics had not appreciably altered. In some other directions, however, I found that there were points which could be elaborated or condensed to advantage; therefore, whilst this is nominally a fourth edition of an old book, it has been extensively revised – and, I trust, thereby improved.

Public taste is not static. There is continual change; and this is as true in the realm of flowers as in other spheres. One reason which gives rise to what might almost be termed fashionable variation of public taste with flowers is that Nature, aided by the hybridist, is continually ringing the changes with new and improved types or varieties. Changing conditions of life, too, affect the popularity of flowers. Nowadays, the average amateur grower has little time to give to a flower which only blooms for a few days in the year, or to one which requires constant care and attention. The flowers of his choice are therefore usually of the foolproof type, easily and inexpensively cultivated. As a general rule, among other attributes, they must be prolific over a lengthy period, and must respond in no half-hearted manner to any extra attention he may give them. If they are as decorative in the home as in the garden, so much the better.

It will be readily seen that all the really popular flowers of today fulfil most of these qualifications. Among them a few stand out clearly as well-nigh ideal, undoubtedly one of the foremost being the subject of this book. The Sweet Pea deserves the title "Queen of Annuals", and one doubts whether there is another flower grown, annual or otherwise, which is so capable of affording its admirers so much pleasure for so little care and expense. It has not always held this proud position in public esteem. In fact, as flowers go, its reign has not been long. Yet in my considered opinion there seems no likelihood of any other annual taking its place in the great heart of the flower-loving public for many years to come. But it is not necessary for me to emphasise unduly points on which I am most probably in complete agreement with my reader.

By comparison, I doubt whether as much has been written about the Sweet Pea in the past 70 years as of most other popular flowers. The demand in this direction has always been ahead of the available literature – even articles in the gardening periodicals have not been so frequent as the flower or its enthusiasts deserve.

I have often been termed a Sweet Pea expert. But though I am now on the wrong side of 90, and since schoolboy days have lived among Sweet Peas, grown them, hybridised them, sold them, and loved them, I now write, not with the feeling that I have assimilated all there is to know about this wonderful flower, but with the firm conviction, which has strengthened as the years have gone by, that there are few subjects about which it is possible to finish learning in a lifetime, especially horticultural subjects. My main object here is to explain modern cultural methods in clear and simple language, and in such a manner that they may readily be adapted to individual requirements and circumstances. However, I fully appreciate the fact that only a comparatively small proportion of readers will be exhibitors, or even potential exhibitors. The great majority love the flower for the pleasure it affords them in their own garden and home. I am hopeful, therefore, that the many pages which I have devoted to topics which have little or nothing to do with culture will be found interesting.

CHARLES W. J. UNWIN

Histon,
Cambridge

CHAPTER I

SWEET PEAS – THEIR ORIGIN, HISTORY AND DEVELOPMENT

A shrewd Dutch friend once gave me a good deal of food for reflection in the casual remark, "None appreciate flowers and gardens more than the English." Though I believe this statement to be perfectly accurate, I hardly feel it comes within the scope of my objectives, either to examine the reasons for this national tendency, or to attempt to analyse the nature of the widespread appeal which flowers exert on all races to greater or lesser degree. It will suffice if we recognise and take for granted their brightening and uplifting influence. Undoubtedly, the love of beautiful things, which is innate and deeply ingrained in the very nature of us all, finds almost complete expression, and even satisfaction, in our admiration of exquisite flowers and lovely gardens. For, after all, what on this earth is more beautiful? Admiration of beauty is individual and somewhat specialised. The builder, the engineer, the printer, the photographer, the artist, the musician and the dress designer will all find beauty in perfect examples of their particular craft, sometimes where the ordinary man in the street would completely fail to recognise it. But the beauty of flowers is, as it were, common ground, something we can all appreciate, whatever our nationality, sex, or age. Music, for example, as I know full well, holds no charm for a few; but I have yet to hear someone say, "I dislike flowers". Perhaps we can only begin to appreciate the full influence and value of flowers if we pause for one moment and try to imagine just what our world would be like without them. It is certainly not surprising that in these strenuous and unsettled times, when the need for relaxation in our leisure hours from the tension of 20th century high pressure is little short of a grave necessity, an ever increasing number have found in the cultivation of flowers a quiet, interesting, refreshing, clean and healthful hobby.

The Sweet Pea provides one of the best examples in horticultural history, not only of the comparatively rapid improvement which can be effected in a flower by the hybridist, but also of the influence on development when Nature herself assists the process in somewhat dramatic fashion. As we know it today the flower bears little resemblance to its ancestors of 200 years ago. It was unknown in England before the end of the 17th century, and we are indebted to Mr. S. B. Dicks for what scant knowledge we possess of its early history. After careful research he found the earliest mention of a Sweet Pea in botanical literature in 1700. The flower certainly came to us from Sicily, and until quite recently Sicily has been considered its home. But I have come across circumstantial evidence which points to another Mediterranean island as its probable birth-place, namely Malta. It would seem that the Sicilian Sweet Peas came first from Malta, and it is a fact that they still grow wild there, whilst there is no record of their ever being found in a wild state in Sicily. However, in 1699 a Sicilian priest named Francis Cupani sent some seeds to a Dr. Uvedale, of Enfield. Unfortunately, it is not very clear what the colour of these first Sweet Peas may have been, but it appears almost certain they were all of the same shade. Very probably the two recorded descriptions, "red standard and blue wings", and just "purple", are neither exactly correct. I surmise the colour was nearer a purple-maroon, possibly a sort of bicolor, with maroon-purple standard and magenta-purple wings, for this is a "throw-back" that one often used to meet in the old days, and one which still crops up occasionally in crosses. What is certain is that the original flowers were quite small, little larger than those of a culinary pea, borne in twos with perhaps an occasional three, and carried on very much shorter stems than in the case of our modern varieties. It is also certain that this Sicilian newcomer was very sweetly and heavily perfumed, also very floriferous. In brief, this is all we really know of its origin and characteristics, but it is quite clear that the value of the flower for cutting, or as a garden subject, was then strictly limited.

We have been unable to find out much more about the Sweet Pea until nearly a century later; but during that time slight changes took place, there was some development, and it would be extremely interesting to know just how this came about, for round about the year 1800 we find not one variety only, but five – the original purple, and in addition a white, black (undoubtedly dark maroon), red, and a pink and white bicolor. These four later varieties may of course have been imported from Sicily, Malta, or elsewhere, and there is the somewhat slim chance that they originated as the result of natural cross-fertilisation. Considering the behaviour of the Sweet Pea in after years, most probably these variations arose quite naturally as mutations or "sports" from the original maroon-purple. (A little later

I will explain what a mutation or "sport" is.) Though we may now admit the slight added advantage which these four new colours would impart, the Sweet Pea even then must have been comparatively unprepossessing, a subject for an odd corner perhaps, a quite ordinary kind of cut flower, or maybe something likely to withstand the curious vicissitudes of the children's garden. It certainly possessed a lovely perfume, and was obviously a member of the pea family, hence the name *Sweet* Pea. I think we can forgive the florists and gardeners of those days for the scant attention they gave it, for it is quite impossible they could have then foreseen its glorious possibilities.

As far as records go, we must now take another big step forward to the latter part of the 19th century, for not until then do we learn of any really serious attempt to improve Sweet Peas. Names like Laxton, Burpee and Eckford, as raisers, prove that both here and in America the flower had by then begun to interest the serious hybridist. To Henry Eckford, who, as long as the flower is known will be gratefully remembered as the "father of the Sweet Pea", should be given the greatest share of credit for the progress then made. Eckford had previously worked on the improvement of other flowers, among them Calceolarias, Cinerarias and Verbenas, but very soon Sweet Peas claimed his entire interest and became his life's work. At the outset it is very doubtful whether Eckford realised the great possibilities or capabilities of the flower; but we can be reasonably sure that his aims were for very definite objectives and that he knew almost exactly what he wanted to attain. The measure of his success was great. For, speaking broadly, it is true that he found the Sweet Pea little known and little valued, and transformed it, in a comparatively short time, into an annual worthy of a place in every garden. By cross-fertilisation and careful selection (work which only those who have experienced it can fully appreciate) he altered the very structure of the flower, eliminating some of its weak points, making it larger and more pleasing to the eye and, further, introduced many of the colours we have at the present time – though not of course in their modern refinement. He left most of its good qualities, varying colour, daintiness of appearance, freedom of flowering, and vigour, either unimpaired or improved. His efforts surely provide a most encouraging example of rapid development of a flower at the hands of the plant breeder, and prompt the fairly obvious surmise that there must surely still be many other flowers capable of responding in like manner, if only patience and judgment are exercised. Ever-increasing public interest came as a direct result of the Eckford improvements. The

Sweet Pea became well known and greatly valued. New varieties, or "Novelties" as they were termed in horticultural circles, were in great demand. Where but a few years previously one would find Sweet Peas only among collections of annuals at Flower Shows, special classes for them were made, and florists began to grow the flower much more extensively as public demand for Sweet Pea cut flowers increased. In 1900 a small band of enthusiasts founded the National Sweet Pea Society in this country – an organisation which ever since then has played a great part in the destiny of the flower. This influential Society and its affiliated Societies have, by exhibitions, conferences, trials of new varieties and literary publications, done much to create, direct and maintain the interest of the general public. On the literary side, a number of experienced horticultural writers have made the Sweet Pea the subject of some excellent books and articles. The pens of E. J. Castle, the brothers Walter and Horace Wright, Thomas Stevenson, William Cuthbertson, T. A. Weston, Charles Curtis, A. J. Macself, H. H. Thomas, Norman Lambert, E. R. Janes, The Rev. D. Gourlay Thomas, and B. R. Jones, among many others, have greatly added to the pleasure of its devotees. In case the reader might consider that Sweet Pea literature has been profuse, one must hasten to add that the period covered by the names I have given is more than half a lifetime.

It was quickly realised that the Sweet Pea generously responded to good methods of cultivation, and that it had then very few drawbacks by way of pests and diseases – factors which were obviously certain to influence gardeners, particularly amateurs, in its favour. Others besides Henry Eckford were devoting considerable attention to raising new varieties, and with no small success, until by the beginning of the 20th century it might have been considered that the flower had almost reached the zenith of its development. Certainly many shades were still open to improvement, whilst in some colours vigour was not all that could be desired. Other flowers, before and since, have reached a similar stage in their development, where, as far as could be judged, further drastic alteration or improvement could not reasonably be expected, and in many such cases a gradual decline in popularity has taken place. Walter P. Wright wrote: "The value of a species lies more in its capacity for producing varietal forms than in its own intrinsic beauty, however great that may be." A sweeping assertion indeed; but my own experience tends to confirm this view very emphatically, particularly from the commercial side of things.

In 1900 the Sweet Pea was thus more or less "marking time", and it is safe to say that no one expected, or was prepared for, a drastic change in form. It should be understood that at that time there was a variation in the outline of flowers of the individual varieties, caused mainly by the difference in shape of the back petal or standard. Perhaps it would be wise at this stage to refer in botanical terms to the parts which make up the Sweet Pea flower itself. Without going into unnecessary detail these are: the tiny stem, on which the bloom is poised; the calyx, which comprises the tiny leaves which protect the petals in the bud stage; the standard, or upright petal at the back; the two wings spread apart just below it; and, in between them, the keel, which is really two petals joined in the shape of a narrow boat-like sheath. The keel envelops and protects the vital fertilising organs of the flower, and the undeveloped seed pod. Let us concentrate our attention for a moment on the standard or back petal, for it is here where the most obvious and important change occurred. Up to 1900 the varieties which made Eckford famous were termed "Grandifloras", or of Grandiflora type, signifying large-flowered, to distinguish them from their smaller predecessors. This term "Grandiflora", as applied to Sweet Peas, has long since lost its original implication. The standards of these Grandifloras varied. Some were more or less hooded or shell-shaped, with a slight inward curl on each side, others were open and flat (as in a culinary pea), sometimes with a cut or notch in the top centre, occasionally with two notches, one on each side, towards the base of the standard. The drastic change in form which occurred in 1901 could be best described as an appreciably larger standard, which was also slightly frilled, crimped, or waved. This was accompanied by a not quite so obvious change in the wings, which became longer, larger, and spread out more widely. The keel too had slightly changed to become larger, wider, and much less closely knit towards its end. We now recognise the new form under the term "open" keel, the old as a "clamped" keel.

This greatly altered form came by means of a mutation or "sport". A mutation may briefly be described as a variation which crops up in a natural manner and not through the influence of cross-fertilisation. At that time there was a very popular pink self, raised by Henry Eckford, called *Prima Donna*, fairly large-flowered, with a slightly hooded standard, the best hooded pink variety of those days, and a vigorous grower which produced plenty of four-bloomed sprays. I think these points are worthy of mention in view of the fact that *Prima Donna* is the progenitor of all our modern Sweet Peas. It had kept true to colour and type for at least eight years before the advent of the waved form and, as far as I am aware, it did not produce the waved mutation again. It is highly probable that during 1901 *Prima Donna* mutated the waved form in a number of gardens, but this was only noticed and selected by Mr. Silas Cole of Althorp Park Gardens, Northampton, by Mr. Eckford at Wem, and by my father, Mr. W. J. Unwin, at Histon. It is not clear what happened to the Wem selection, but Mr. Cole saved not only his selection, but named and introduced it as *Countess Spencer*. From this name is derived the term "Spencer type". The Histon selection, which my father saved, was introduced under the name of *Gladys Unwin*, and later proved to be slightly different from *Countess Spencer* in that the flowers were not quite as large or wavy as Mr. Cole's novelty. *Gladys Unwin* might perhaps be termed an intermediate type, midway between the Spencer and Grandiflora types – in fact, varieties which sprang from it, such as *Nora Unwin* or *Frank Dolby*, were given the distinguishing name of "Unwin type". At first there was keen, indeed almost heated, rivalry between the Spencer and Unwin types. Whereas the Unwin varieties were true to type and colour, many of the early Spencers were unfixed. Again, by comparison, the Unwins were a little more robust and free-flowering in habit. However, the larger, more wavy form of the Spencers quickly became the more popular, and except in the pedigrees of many of the better Spencers, varieties of Unwin type comparatively soon disappeared. I will not dwell on *Gladys Unwin* and its immediate progeny, except to say that the finding of *Gladys Unwin* led directly to the foundation of the seed business of which I am now the senior member, for it turned my father's business activities from the cut flower trade to the seed trade. Fortunately, the late Professor Sir Rowland Biffen, the world-famed wheat hybridist, was living at Histon at this time, and it was on his advice, and through his practical instruction and guidance, that my father began hybridising Sweet Peas. This led directly to what ultimately proved his greatest interest, for from that time until he died in 1947 my father's plant breeding operations extended over a wide field, embracing many flowers and some vegetables, with marked success. It gives me a good deal of personal pleasure to record gratefully the contact which we kept with Sir Rowland Biffen up to the time of his death, and the value we always placed on his comments, criticism, and advice on those subjects which attracted his interest.

It will be obvious that the advent of the new waved type opened up wonderful opportunities for the hybridist, since it was a comparatively simple matter to transfer this new frilliness and size of flower quickly to other colours. In consequence, a multitude of new Spencer type varieties was introduced. Many of these varieties were almost identical, if not quite; and in their haste to supply an increasing demand raisers were tempted to introduce new varieties before they were properly "fixed". (By "fixed" I mean that they came true to colour and form. On the other hand, "unfixed" implies that they did not breed true, either to colour, or form, or both.) Whilst this unstable tendency caused disappointment, it in no way stemmed the quickly rising popularity of the flower. Indeed, such was the measure of public interest that Lord Northcliffe, then the owner of the *Daily Mail*, gave a £1,000 First Prize and other large sums for a single small bunch of Sweet Peas. His original intention was to give £1,000 for a single spike only, and only the pressure of advice from my father and other experts – who foresaw the impossibility of judging accurately the vast number of single spikes which would be entered – caused him to change. At this great *Daily Mail* Sweet Pea Competition I watched the judges at work in the old Crystal Palace on the many thousands of bunches which were entered, a truly colossal task, but even this was child's play compared with what would have happened had the original plan been carried into effect. As might be expected, this magnificent prize, and the publicity which accompanied it, focussed public attention on the flower, and introduced its beauty and value to a very large number who had not previously realised what it was really like.

Admittedly it may be guess-work on my part, but probably between three and four thousand names have been bestowed on varieties of Sweet Peas in the past. Not that these represented as many different shades, for a number were identical to older varieties, whilst others have shown only very minor variation in colour, size, form or vigour. The very great majority have had but a short life, quickly passing out of existence; but even so, at any one period, including the present moment, there were between 350 and 500 varieties in commerce, including all classes and types. From time to time writers have bewailed the large number of names and varieties and the confusion this causes in the minds of all growers, more particularly beginners. It has been claimed that there should be some kind of official restriction or control on the introduction of new varieties, in order to lessen considerably the number, and to prevent the introduction of any Novelty of little or no value. It has also been suggested many times that a drastic "weeding out" should be made of existing older varieties that are redundant. In theory these ideas seem sound, steps

Winning exhibit for the coveted 'Daily Mail Cup'.
Courtesy of J.R.F. Bishop

in the right direction, yet one hesitates to support such action. Public opinion provides a gauge or test which, though not immediate in effect, ultimately and very surely winnows the grain from the chaff. It is an undoubted fact that only the very best Novelties ever become popular. Experience also proves that no selected body or committee of experts can accurately reflect public opinion. In Sweet Peas, as in many other horticultural subjects, there are several examples of new varieties obtaining the highest awards, and yet afterwards failing to attract public favour. On the other hand, there are just as many examples of Novelties failing to obtain any recognition at trials or elsewhere, but which later have become firm public favourites for considerable periods. Therefore, with all its faults, I am in favour of the present system, whereby all new varieties in Sweet Peas and other flowers are left to this vast public winnowing machine, with no restriction on output other than the raisers' judgment and reputation. After all, there is in existence a very effective check on the introduction of unworthy Novelties, imposed by the adverse reflection on the

Cream Southbourne A good show bench variety. Raised by Rev. T.K. Colledge.

Old Fashioned Mixed The old grandiflora Sweet Peas, very sweetly scented.

status of the raiser concerned. Yet another argument could be advanced against the theory of restriction, for surely any kind of outside control would tend to irritate and handicap the work of the raisers. In short, I favour the present method of giving the raiser a free hand, permitting his reputation to depend mainly on the success of his efforts. I am very much against anything and everything that might tend to detract from the free development and improvement of the flower.

The views expressed here do not imply that I am opposed in any way to official trials of new varieties, provided these are grown properly and judged honestly by disinterested people. Publicity given to the flower and to successful Novelties is all to the good, and in fairness it must be said that only rarely is a really first-class new variety overlooked by trials judges. On the other hand there are not a great many instances in the past of an inferior variety being honoured. It is safe to say that, if ten chosen committees judged the same set of trials on the same day, the findings of every committee would differ. Again, the same committee judging the same trials on two different dates, separated by not less than 14 days, would also produce different results. A committee composed entirely of ladies would probably arrive at results a good deal different from an all male committee, and in the same way the results with the same seedlings at the N.S.P.S. Trials and the Scottish N.S.P.S. Trials always vary considerably. All this goes to prove that 100 per cent accuracy is not a practical possibility, though the degree of accuracy usually attained most definitely makes properly conducted trials well worthwhile. To offset those disappointments which are inevitable, raisers who send new seedlings to official trails would do well never to overlook that element of chance or "luck" which is an ever-present factor to be reckoned with.

It would be extremely difficult, perhaps quite impossible, to enumerate all individuals and all firms who have, since the time of Henry Eckford, assisted in bringing the Sweet Pea to its present state of perfection, but such a list would certainly include many famous names. As might be expected, traders have contributed the lion's share, though the successes of a few amateur raisers in the past stand out in one's memory. Among the latter I would include Dr. H. T. Hinton, Alex Malcolm, The Rev. D. Gourlay Thomas, and J. H. Taylor. All these are British; but I am not sure whether J. A. Bland of Canada should best be classified as an amateur or a trader. In any case he has a few good varieties to his credit. Among the American raisers, W. Atlee Burpee Co., the Ferry Morse Seed Co., the Wm. Macdonald Seed Co., the Denholm Seed Co. and the Waller-Franklin Seed Co., have made the greatest contribution of any traders outside these islands. It is, however, from within the British Isles that the bulk of good Sweet Pea Novelties of the Late Spencer type have come from trade raisers.

Is the Sweet Pea as popular now as in the past? Undoubtedly, at the moment less seed is being sold here than just prior to the First World War, but one doubts whether the total number of growers is much smaller. During the War years many seed firms in this country gave up supplying named varieties. Sweet Pea seed became comparatively very expensive, even the mixtures, and for other obvious reasons a large proportion ceased to grow Sweet Peas. Fortunately this picture has greatly changed, and I do not think present public interest in the flower is appreciably smaller than at any period in the past. As I am attempting to deal with the future of the flower in the concluding chapter, I will defer that line of thought for the moment, with the brief claim that the future of the flower seems assured, for the simple and sufficient reason that, by comparison, there is nothing on the horticultural horizon likely to take its place.

Where climatic conditions allow, other countries have followed us in their interest in Sweet Peas, in proportion to the interest they take in flowers in general. Before the last World War, most of the Sweet Peas sold in this country came from California and still do. David Lemmon of California, the famous raiser of the Jet Set, Early Mammoth, Royal, Supersnoop and other types of Sweet Peas, is an old friend. He has also raised excellent new varieties of other kinds of flowers. He came to see our Trials last August and I had a most interesting talk with him. His greatest ambition is to raise a new type of Sweet Pea which is completely heat resistant. He said this would more than double the popularity of the Sweet Pea, for there are many countries in the world, including most of America and Canada, where high temperatures prevent the successful growing of any of our existing types. What an excellent project! I hope he gets that new race, and feel sure that he will.

CHAPTER II

TYPES OR CLASSES OF SWEET PEAS

Though each possess sub-divisions, we can divide modern Sweet Peas into three distinct main classes or types: the original tall types, the Dwarfs, and the Early or Winter-flowering types. I will examine each of them in turn.

I. THE TALL TYPES

There are now many different tall-growing races of Sweet Peas – too many to mention all of them. The type most popular here, with which this book is mainly concerned, is the original type, now universally called the Late Spencer type. I will deal with the best of its modern varieties in a later chapter. American raisers have given us almost all of these variations and it is fitting to give their names: Anton Zvolanek & Son, Bodgers, the Denholm Seed Co., D. M. Ferry & Co. and the Ferry Morse Co. are responsible for most of them. The most popular of these types is the Galaxy, a multi-flowering type. By multi-flowering I mean plants which will produce flower stems with four to nine blooms with ordinary culture. Those generally available here are the Cuthbertson, Floribunda race raised by Frank Cuthbertson, who emigrated to America after working for Dobbies of Edinburgh. The Cuthbertsons are still used by cut flower market British growers.

There is also the Early Multiflora Gigantea type, an earlier flowering form of Galaxy, which has now been surpassed by the Mammoth series of varieties, larger-flowered and longer-stemmed.

II. THE DWARF AND SEMI-DWARF TYPES

The chief characteristic of these types is that they are very dwarf in habit, only attaining a height of about six inches when in bloom. Their growth is very short jointed, their habit bushy. Whilst the flowers are almost as large as those of the tall varieties, they are borne in twos and threes on extremely short stems. The type originated in the same way

Jet-Set Mixed A semi-dwarf variety with more than four good size blooms to a stem.

as *Countess Spencer*, namely through a mutation which was discovered by Messrs. Morse & Co. (now the Ferry Morse Seed Co.) in California in 1894. The original dwarfs were given the name Cupids. They first came among tall plants, and were white-seeded whites; though Messrs. Morse found a pink dwarf the following year. Two years later the original white Cupid gave a few cream-coloured "rogues" or "sports", all these three colours being of the plain or Grandiflora type of flower. Later, they were hybridised with one another, and with tall varieties, both Grandifloras and Spencers, and it was found that these crosses gave results in Mendelian proportions. Further, the dwarfness being a recessive characteristic, all the dwarf progeny bred and remained true dwarfs, though quite a large number of colours were produced. (The Mendel proportions mentioned will be fully explained later.)

At no time has the Cupid type made the slightest headway in this country; nor can it be said that they are very popular in America or elsewhere. In the first place they inevitably suffer by comparison with the ordinary type. Their short stems make them quite useless as cut flowers, so their value is reduced, of necessity, either to bedding, edging, or as pot plants. On many occasions I have grown them experimentally, and find a great tendency for their buds to drop off before opening if the weather is at all wet or cold. The Cupids are very much more affected with bud-dropping than the tall varieties in adverse weather, possibly through their foliage and buds being so close to the surface of the soil. Even with everything in their favour, faded flowers or seed pods must be regularly removed, or they quickly cease to bloom. Then there are so many other subjects much more suitable for pots or window boxes, that very rarely has one ever heard of a grower consistently using them as pot plants. However, I believe that in some parts of America and elsewhere, where the summer is long and the rainfall slight, they are seen to better advantage, even under conditions which prove too trying for either of the tall types. In spite of all this, I must confess that these little Cupids exercise a sort of mild fascination for me. I cannot put them on one side and forget them. In consequence, and against my better judgment, every now and again I sow a few pots for the greenhouse, or find a border edge I think might suit them.

An American writer once described the conditions necessary for the culture of Cupid Sweet Peas as "rather dry, moderately rich soil, a hot dry season, good cultivation, and the prompt removal of all withered flowers and pods". I am afraid I am unable to find any reason why this type should deserve a greater measure of public esteem, and my best advice to the reader is not to give them garden or greenhouse room except perhaps as curiosities. In 1951, I grew two new variations of the Cupid type from the McDonald Seed Co. of California, one a deep navy-blue, the other a silvery pink. Both grew 18 to 24 inches high, and needed short supports to keep them upright. They flowered quite freely, and were no more prone to drop their buds than the ordinary type. Four large pots in the cold greenhouse made a sufficiently good display for my wife to move two of them into the dining room. Clumps in a mixed border and near a rockery also were colourful for a lengthy period. It is early days to judge what the future of this "taller Cupid" development may be, but I must say that I was very favourably impressed. It is unfair to compare the dwarfs with ordinary tall Sweet Peas. The correct approach, difficult though this may be, would be to judge them on their own merit as a garden or pot plant, completely ignoring their comparative shortcomings in other directions.

III. THE EARLY OR WINTER-FLOWERING TYPES

Like the Cupids, the Early-flowering race did not originate by means of hybridisation, though it has been greatly improved by this process. Plants which flowered much earlier than the ordinary type have appeared as natural mutations or "sports" in America, Algeria and

Australia, and in each country they have been saved separately and improved by crossing, first with the Grandiflora type, later with the Spencer type. In America, such well-known seed firms as D. M. Ferry & Co., Zvolanek, and later on W. Atlee Burpee & Co., the Ferry Morse Seed Co., the Denholm Seed Co., and the Waller-Franklin Seed Co. have all contributed to their improvement. The Rev. Edwin Arkwright of Telemly, Algiers, Africa, Arthur Yates & Co., Anderson & Co., and H. C. Mott of Australia, have also raised Early-flowering strains of their own, closely resembling the American varieties.

More recently, Frank G. Cuthbertson of the Ferry Morse Seed Co. has introduced the latest development of the Early-flowering type, giving his name to this particular class. It appears that he noticed a particularly strong and vigorous plant among the seedlings on which he was working, which also produced extra long stems. The colour was poor, but he crossed this seedling with the best varieties of the Early-flowering type, and as a result obtained a wide range of colours. In California the Cuthbertson Sweet Peas bloom three weeks earlier than the ordinary type, whilst it is claimed that, by comparison, they have greater vigour, longer stems, bloom for a longer period, and that their colours are clearer and brighter. This may perhaps be true of their behaviour in California; but, in spite of the fact that seedlings from this new type have already been extremely successful at the Scottish N.S.P.S. Trials, gaining Gold and Silver Medals as well as First Class Certificates, I still have an open mind with regard to their prospects in this country. It is quite "on the cards" that they may eventually prove an advance on the ordinary type here; but the Early-flowering type has not so far made a serious challenge, and I would like to have the benefit of more experience of the Cuthbertson Sweet Peas here before coming to any really definite opinion on this point. At the Scottish Trials they bloomed ten days earlier than the ordinary Spencers – a difference which I think would be a little more marked the further south they were grown. At the moment I am much more impressed by their claims of greater vigour, clearer, brighter colours, and longer flowering period, than their earliness. It would seem that we must regard their trials successes at most as a challenge, but certainly not as definite proof that they may ultimately usurp the position held for so long by the older ordinary race. The Cuthbertson race is making some headway here, and I was told in Holland that they are rapidly becoming popular on the Continent as cut flowers among commercial growers. Their length of stem appears to be

Patio Mixed A very dwarf, very full bushy plant suitable for tubs and window boxes.

largely responsible for this. In America their popularity has increased by leaps and bounds; but whether this is largely at the expense of the ordinary type or the older Early-flowering type is not very clear.

Without a doubt, and apart altogether from the Cuthbertson race, the best modern Early-flowering varieties are now equal in form, size of bloom, and length of stem, to the best of the ordinary type. Further, the colour range too is almost as wide. During one hot, dry summer some years ago, I saw a number of the Early-flowering kinds among the trials of one of the big Essex wholesale seed firms. Admittedly the season favoured them, but they were very, very good, and had I not been told I should not have known that they were Early-flowering. As far back as 1923, in their annual report, the Floral Committee of the National Sweet Pea Society, of which I was then a member, gave this terse verdict: "With regard to the Winter or Early-flowering varieties, your Committee is of the opinion that this type of Sweet Peas is of little use in this country." Though my more recent experience would tend somewhat to shake the uncompromising opinion to which I subscribed all those years ago, and making all due allowances for improvement in the meantime, I still think that we must pin our faith on the ordinary type in this country. Given the same treatment, they have the advantage of coming into bloom weeks earlier than the ordinary type. But, unless drastic changes have occurred fairly recently, they will not (apart from the Cuthbertsons) grow as tall, and their flowering period is shorter. In this country, I still consider their main use is for indoor culture, where early blooms from Christmas onwards are required. As a matter of fact they are grown fairly extensively here in this way, but not in such quantity as in America. In the U.S.A. and a number of other countries, in districts where the original type are hopeless failures owing to climatic conditions, the Early-flowering type deservedly enjoys a very high measure of public esteem, and it can be said that they have done much to popularise the Sweet Pea where the original type is a sheer impossibility. Sub-tropical and semi-arid conditions suit them best. As I see it, that is the picture of the comparative merit of the two.

It will be gathered that interest in the Early-flowering types in this country has been comparatively slight and decidedly critical. Raisers have strenuously avoided introducing any Early-flowering "blood" into their crosses. As far as I am aware, practically no new varieties have been raised here, though Professor Sir Rowland Biffen, round about 1904, raised an early white self called *Zero* from a cross between the ordinary type *Nora Unwin* and the Early-flowering *Mont Blanc.* I have not attempted of late years to try many of the Early-flowering varieties on cordons, but remember that years ago, under this method, they were distinguished from the ordinary type by somewhat short habit of growth, comparatively narrow and sparse foliage, and by the tendency to throw few, if any, lateral or side shoots, more particularly in the early stages of their growth. These differences are much less marked in modern Early-flowering varieties.

CHAPTER III

GENERAL CULTURAL REMARKS

In the first wireless talk ever given on Sweet Peas, which I had the pleasure of addressing to listeners from the London Studio of the B.B.C. as long ago as 16th October 1923, I introduced the subject as follows, and venture to repeat that introduction, for what I said then is just as true today: "So much has been written and said on the subject of Sweet Pea culture that I am convinced many would-be growers are scared away, for they imagine the flower a difficult one to grow. The simple facts of the matter are these: the Sweet Pea is one of the very easiest, most adaptable, and most reasonable flowers we have, and can be successfully grown by anyone. Don't be frightened by elaborate cultural instructions, for if you can grow eating peas or runner beans, you can grow Sweet Peas. Almost any soil will be found suitable for obtaining a wealth of good blooms for garden and house decoration, even if only dug over and no more time or money spent on it than on any ordinary flower or vegetable crop. Not the least of the virtues of the Sweet Pea is its ready response to good culture; it is *the* flower for the million, and to the ordinary flower-lover, with little time and facility for intensive culture, it affords greater results in proportion to the care bestowed upon it than any other flower in existence."

Cultural methods depend to a great extent on the object for which one grows Sweet Peas, to a lesser degree on one's facilities and circumstances. The greatest possible number of blooms per plant can be attained by giving individual plants sufficient space above and below ground to develop in a natural manner. On the other hand, sheer quality and size are produced by the somewhat artificial "cordon" system, fully explained in the next chapter. Apart from this, the Sweet Pea is most adaptable, capable of rising to almost any occasion, in a manner unsurpassed by few, if any, other flowers in existence. It can be successfully grown in rows or in clumps, in tubes, boxes or pots, in the greenhouse or the open ground, on the roof garden, and even – by using the Cupid type – in a window box. By utilising both the Early or Winter-flowering type, and the ordinary well-known Summer type, flowers can be produced nearly the whole year round, under glass and in the open.

As we have seen, the development of the Sweet Pea itself has been comparatively rapid. Methods of culture too have changed, but more slowly, and it may be that we have now almost reached our limit in this particular direction. Though it is true that rules of good culture cannot be laid down which may be followed blindly, with little or no exercise of judgment and commonsense on the part of the grower, in broad outline good cultural methods are almost standardised. Experts may differ on details, due in the main to conditions of soil and localities, but all follow much the same procedure. Experience alone will provide the final touches, but I do emphatically assure the beginner that there are now no obscure secrets of culture, no closely guarded methods practised by a few, and certainly no cultural "stunts" that will turn a novice into an expert overnight.

CHAPTER IV

THE CORDON OR EXHIBITION METHOD OF CULTURE

The best place in the garden for a Sweet Pea plot is an open sunny position, preferably where there is a good depth of topsoil and where you know from experience that you usually obtain good results from other crops. If sheltered from north and east winds, so much the better. It should be borne in mind that, if possible, the rows ought to run north to south (though this is not essential) and that good drainage is an undoubted asset. For double rows, preparing the soil sixteen to eighteen inches deep and in strips three to four feet wide is ample. On no account should the natural position of the soil layers be interfered with. It is important to keep the topsoil on the top and let the subsoil remain underneath. All digging and soil preparation needs to be completed before Christmas, the earlier the better, for *Sweet Peas love a really firm settled root-run.*

On many occasions I have seen really excellent, well-balanced spikes produced from cordon plants grown on ground which had only been dug one "spit" deep. (A "spit" is the length of the tines of the fork, or the blade of the spade being used.) However, most exhibitors work their Sweet Pea site two "spits" deep. All that this really means is simple double digging, adding whatever manures or fertilisers one decides to use as the work proceeds. The method can be throwing the top spit on one side, breaking up the lower spit where it lies, or alternatively using the "step" method, throwing the top spit forward. Strips three to four feet wide will suffice with well-drained light to medium soils. But if the soil is too heavy, or slow to drain, it is advisable to double dig the entire site, even if manuring is limited to the strips where the rows are to come. It is best to break up large clods as far as practicable, but to leave the surface quite rough until early spring. Though Sweet Peas can be grown successfully on the same site for many years, it is advisable to "ring the changes" by reversing the positions of rows and paths every year or two.

We consider next the nature or character of the plant. Comparatively speaking, the Sweet Pea grows quickly and luxuriantly above ground, producing flowers and new growth over a long period. The root system is naturally extensive and wide-searching; so we must not only provide the facility for it to develop freely but also ensure that there is sufficient food available *at the time the plant needs it most.* The question of what manures to use, and in what quantities, cannot be answered offhand, for the simple reason that it all depends on the fertility of the ground, that is, on what available feeding agents are there already. Here, an analysis of the soil can often be of great help. This can easily be done with a soil test kit, obtainable from most stores that sell garden sundries. Undoubtedly *over-manuring is much worse than under-manuring.* Nothing can be done quickly enough to remedy the adverse effects of the former. During the flowering period additional help can be given should the plants need it.

I am, however, not ashamed to own that I am rather old-fashioned about manures. I prefer to get them from the farmyard, sty or stable, rather than the fertiliser factory. So my advice is to use good well-made (that is, fairly well-rotted) animal manure. Whether it is cow, horse, sheep or mixed farmyard manure does not greatly matter. As I have said, soils vary in the kinds and quantities of manures and fertilisers they need. But let us suppose we are dealing with the needs of an average kind of soil which has not been manured heavily for two or three years. As you move and work the second or lower "spit", mix in a liberal dressing, not more than a barrow load of manure to every three square yards of the second or lower "spit", but do not mix any animal manure in the top "spit". At the same time also mix in (if possible) plenty of bone meal at the rate of three or four handfuls per square yard throughout the whole working, including the top "spit". I emphasise the word "mix"; *never* place manures or fertilisers in layers, sandwich fashion. I also like to mix in throughout a good dressing of dried natural seaweed fertiliser, for, like bonemeal, it is perfectly safe and also contains most of the trace elements so essential to plant life. Leave the surface of the soil quite rough to obtain the benefits of wintering. In January or February, broadcast a moderate dressing of hydrated lime over the surface. If the soil has been limed during the previous year or two, omit liming and apply a light dressing of a good compound general garden fertiliser a fortnight or three weeks before planting out. Of course if the ground is in really good heart neither lime nor fertiliser are by any means essential. At a favourable time in the new year, fork over the surface once or twice, breaking up any clods and pulverising the top few inches down to a fine condition.

Autumn-sown plants overwintered in pots ready for planting out.

Treading about will also help to settle the ground and give the firm rooting medium that suits Sweet Peas.

Farmers and gardeners today use a far greater number of chemical products, weedkillers and pesticides than they did twenty years ago. Toolsheds have taken on the appearance of a chemist's shop. Many of the chemicals used have made life easier for the farmer and gardener; but there are some which have not. Firstly, unless care is taken with weedkillers, ordinary and selective, it is all too easy to get them or their fumes distributed where they damage or kill plants which one wants saved. Unwins sometimes receive letters from customers asking what has caused the trouble with their plants. It is not often disease but the characteristic and easily recognisable distortion of plants which is caused by weedkillers. Secondly, farmyard and stable manures can be contaminated by toxic chemicals. These kill off all plant life on the sites on which they are used. The obvious way of avoiding this state of affairs is not to use any animal manure but to keep to other fertilisers and home-made compost. There are still some farmers who avoid using chemicals and one is fortunate if there is one nearby.

With fertile soil in good heart, it is usually advisable to reduce the quantity of manures and fertilisers after the first year and occasionally to omit them altogether for a year. Soils vary considerably and after a proper balance of nutrients has been achieved, it is all too easy to upset that balance by over-manuring. As to what constitutes a proper balance, I think the quality of the blooms produced the previous summer will be a good guide, and experience a better one.

In some rather exceptional cases, mainly in kitchen gardens where the soil has been generously treated in past years, I have seen very fine, well-balanced spikes produced after digging one spit deep and no manure or fertiliser added. However, almost all soils will need some help, and good, well-made compost will almost take the place of animal manure. I would, in fact, prefer good compost to poor manure. Failing this, humus could be provided by using a good dressing of peat or hop manure, with the addition of a good compound Sweet Pea Fertiliser or maybe a little, but only a little, poultry, rabbit or pigeon manure, should any of these be available. As already mentioned, a soil analysis at the outset can often prove invaluable in letting the grower know what he is "up against".

By far the smallest expense involved in growing any crop (including Sweet Peas) is the cost of the seed itself, and it pays over and over again to get your seed from a reputable source. Obtain good varieties of good quality, for, after all, these cost no more to grow than the others. In the Midlands and South of England, most successful exhibitors sow in autumn in cold frames during the first fortnight in October, the actual time depending on the district. In the North of England and Scotland, they rely mainly on sowing in January or February in slight warmth under glass, or in cold frames or a cold greenhouse in late February and early March.

Any ordinary sweet garden soil is usually quite good enough for growing Sweet Peas, but it should be sifted to take out stones or clods and a little sand mixed in if it is not sufficiently porous. However, I must add that, in the long run, it pays to use a slightly more elaborate compost, or a "home-made" mixture of four parts loam to one part each of peat and sand. Of late I have been pleased with results from using John Innes No. 2. The great thing is to make sure that the compost is in a moist condition when sowing. Use pots or boxes, sowing the seed half to three-quarters of an inch deep and allowing five to seven seeds to a five-inch pot, or two inches each way to each seed if boxes are used. Crock the bottoms of pots and ensure good drainage with boxes. Water lightly through a fine rose after sowing and, to retain moisture, cover the pots or boxes with glass, polythene or brown paper for a few days until the seedlings show through the surface, *then remove the covering immediately*. Throughout the period whilst they are in their pots or boxes, avoid over-watering. To protect the roots of autumn-sown pots, plunge the pots or boxes to their rims in peat, soil or weathered ashes, and after the seedlings appear, remove the frame-lights entirely, only replacing them when the weather is very wet or when a hard frost threatens, for *light frosts will not harm them.* During a hard, prolonged frost, additional protection can be given by placing mats, tarpaulins, sacks, or a layer of straw over the frame-lights. However, it is vitally important not to remove this covering until the soil in the pots has completely thawed out, slowly, gently and without any assistance. Giving all the light and air possible will ensure hardy, sturdy plants.

Healthy seedlings with extensive root growth showing nitrogen fixing nodules.

Pinching out young seedlings at two leaf pair stage.
Courtesy of Practical Gardening

Sweet Pea seeds vary in colour, size and the texture of their seed coat in the different varieties. The seed coats of some of the mottled and black-seeded varieties are hard and somewhat impervious to moisture, and "chipping" hastens germination. "Chipping" simply means the removal of a tiny portion of the seed-coat with a sharp penknife or file, taking care to avoid the "eye" or scar on the seed. To save time, some growers soak the mottled and black-seeded kinds overnight and then, just before sowing, chip the few which have not swollen. The white, brown and wrinkled varieties *must not be chipped.* A few varieties termed "soft-seeded" behave in exactly the opposite manner to the hard-skinned kinds; the colour of their seed coat is usually light chocolate. They have the annoying tendency, to greater or lesser degree, of rotting during germination, more particularly if soil conditions are a little too cold or too moist. With these soft-seeded varieties a good germination may be expected if a liberal proportion of peat is mixed with the potting soil and the pots or boxes are not watered until germination has taken place. Germination difficulties should not be allowed to cause alarm. Most likely a good germination will be achieved with all varieties if the advice given above is followed and if the seeds are neither "chipped" nor soaked.

We used to get trouble sometimes with soft-seeded varieties and then, somewhat sceptically, tried dressing the seed. Since then, with all sowings, autumn and spring, we have dressed the seed and never – touch wood – had germination trouble. Seed dressings are inexpensive and should be used sparingly, for a little will go a long way. Further, they will remain good for years if stored and kept in a dry place. It is a good plan to set one or two break-back mousetraps, baited with breadcrust, on top of the pots or boxes immediately after sowing, for all too often the seedsman gets the blame for germination failures when mice are the real culprits. Of late years, in some districts, sparrows will eat the seedlings as soon as they appear and netting seems to be the only effective remedy. Slugs or snails can be prevented from attacking them by scattering a few slug pellets in the frame.

Until they are planted out, young Sweet Pea seedlings need very little attention. They should not be "coddled". *The great secret is to grow them along slowly, hardily and sturdily.* Too much water at their roots is likely to do them more harm than hard frosts. The plant is naturally hardy, but you can easily "fuss" it into becoming tender. Many exhibitors re-pot their seedlings singly into three-inch pots (using the same sort of soil as for sowing) during a favourable spell of weather in November, December or January. This facilitates planting out with the ball of soil intact, which with no disturbance of the roots is particularly advantageous on heavy land. On the other hand, I would never claim that re-potting is essential. Experience has proved that it is not wise to rely on the original or seed growth when growing for exhibition. The growth or "leader" to be ultimately retained should be the strongest of the side shoots which will spring from the base of the plants. To encourage the formation of these side shoots most growers pinch out the extreme tips of the seed growth after the second or third pair of leaves are formed. Pinching can be done with fingers or, better still, with scissors, usually during December with autumn-sown seedlings, but it can be delayed until February if side shoots appear to be developing naturally and freely. Pinch spring-sown seedlings when their second or third pair of leaves has fully developed.

Because Sweet Peas are climbers, it is necessary to support them. In exhibition culture, most growers use eight-foot bamboo canes, but osier-rods or even cord netting will answer. The main thing is to erect a framework of posts and (with double rows) cross-pieces of wood with stout strands of wire connecting them sufficiently firmly and

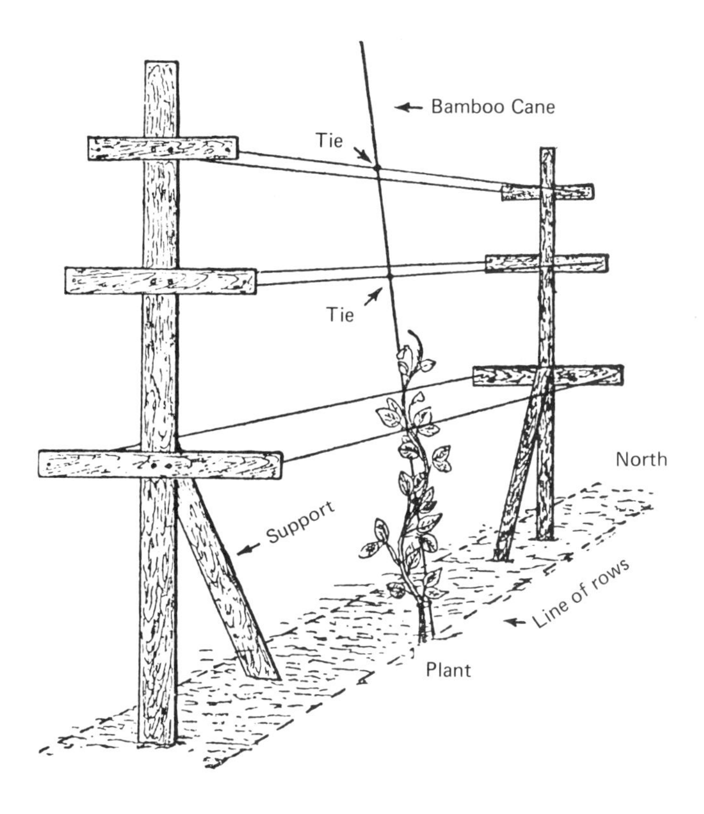

rigidly to withstand wind. The canes – or other supports – are then securely tied to the wires just before the seedlings are planted out. There are all sorts of variations of the post, cross-piece and wire type of framework, and I would say that whatever may be the least expensive and most convenient to the individual concerned is the best. Incidentally, the wooden cross-pieces should be a few inches shorter than the width of the double rows, so as to allow the canes to slope slightly inwards.

As far as planting out is concerned, the actual time will vary with the locality, the soil, and weather conditions. But generally speaking, with autumn-sown seedlings, the first favourable spell in March is about right. To economise in ground space, use double rows, a minimum of twelve inches apart, with a "pathway" of about four feet between them. Eight inches should be the distance allowed from plant to plant, and it is advisable to insert and fasten up the canes in proper position before planting so as to avoid damaging the roots.

Removing side shoots from cordon grown Sweet Peas.
Courtesy of Practical Gardening

Plant at the front or side of the canes for, when the time comes, this facilitates "dropping" or lowering of the plants. (I will explain this lowering procedure later.) With single plants in small pots, loosen or untwine the coil of roots at the bottom, but otherwise plant with the ball of soil intact, keeping the point where the first "break" or side shoot emerges on a level with the surface. With several plants in a pot, gently knead the ball of soil with the hands and then carefully shake away the soil and disentangle the roots. Treat plants from boxes in the same way. Use a trowel or small spade for planting, spreading out the roots. *Always plant firmly.* Place twigs around each plant to keep them from blowing about. One other important tip: never plant a seedling which has a brown "collar" on the white part of the stem above the seed, for within a few weeks these invariably collapse suddenly and prematurely. It has been found also that the use of a seed dressing greatly minimises the risk of brown "collars" on the plants.

Growth should not be restricted or pruned until the plants are nine to twelve inches high. The strongest "leader" or growth on each plant should be selected, and the remaining basal side shoots or growth should be removed carefully with scissors or knife. Tie this leader loosely to its cane, leaving ample room for the haulm to thicken out. Growth will then be fairly rapid, and from this stage onwards all tendrils and side shoots – which latter will form in every leaf axil – should be removed regularly when quite tiny with finger and thumb. The term "cordon" comes from these restrictive operations. All we are doing is restricting growth above ground to one main stem or haulm and at the same time encouraging as extensive a root system as possible. It naturally follows that all growth above ground – leaves, stems and blooms – will naturally be very much larger than if the plant was allowed to develop naturally in its own sweet way. Thus we get quality rather than quantity – a smaller number of flowers, but larger and finer. The first few flower stems should not be allowed to develop. Pinch them out when very tiny and wait until little stems appear with four buds before they are allowed to develop and flower.

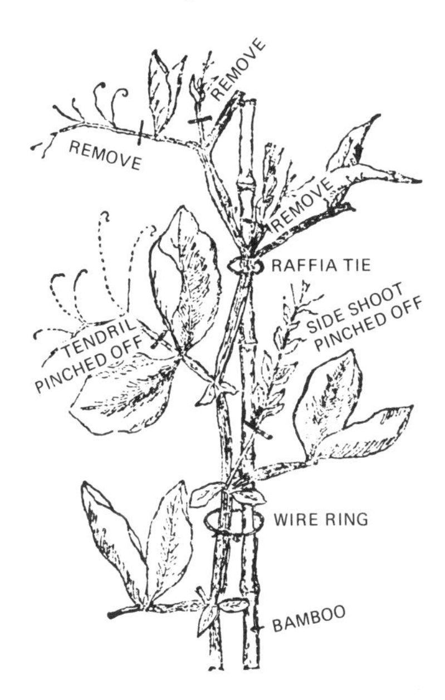

I would advise the beginner to keep to this maximum restriction – one "leader" to each plant – until he obtains some experience of the behaviour of individual varieties on his soil. Varieties certainly differ in their natural vigour. With experience it will probably be found that a few extra vigorous varieties will give better balanced spikes if two "leaders" are allowed to each plant instead of one. This does not mean that the distance from plant to plant must be increased when planting out or the number of canes doubled. Plant as advised and fasten both "leaders" to the one cane. Another method of "putting the brake" on excessive vigour, at any period of growth, is to allow side shoots partly to develop. Instead of rubbing or pinching them out when tiny, let them get two or three inches long and then nip out their growing tips, leaving one pair of leaves to develop on each. Experience will be your best guide, but it is safe to experiment with these modifications of restriction, *on a few plants only*, if required, to test whether they give better quality spikes on the very vigorous varieties.

Unless conditions are very exceptional, the plants should not be watered or fed until they are well in flower and not even then if this can safely be avoided. It is much better to rely mainly on a "good foundation" when preparing and manuring the soil, rather than feeding later on. If feeding is necessary, use the old-fashioned liquid manure and soot water, made by suspending a bag containing cow or sheep manure and soot in a tube of water for a few days. Dilute this well with water when applying it, roughly until its colour is about the same as that of very pale ale. As an alternative, or for a change of diet, use a special compound Sweet Pea fertiliser of a good brand, a seaweed fertiliser, or a reliable general purpose fertiliser such as "Phostrogen"; but make a point of giving *less* than the makers recommend, to be on the safe side. The best method of watering or liquid feeding is through the spout of the can into shallow drills drawn with a hoe about eight inches from the plants, afterwards levelling the soil with a rake. Feeding once every twelve or fourteen days is ample, whilst watering of course depends entirely on rainfall. Overfeeding is something like giving a baby a beefsteak, and it is so terribly easy to "ruin the digestion" of cordon-grown plants in this way. Always keep on the safe side.

It is taken as read that, as a matter of routine management, hoeing around the plants is undertaken regularly, to check weeds and conserve moisture. *But it is important not to hoe deeply.* If the soil is light and the season hot and dry, a surface mulch of short well-decayed manure or even peat and spent hops placed round the plants is most helpful and keeps the roots cool. Some growers simply use a thin layer of straw. Mulching does away with the necessity for hoeing, and many good exhibitors apply a mulch regularly every season during May or early June. It is also assumed that there will be no negligence in tying up the plants regularly, say twice a week, pinching out all side shoots and tendrils with finger and thumb when quite tiny. It is best to carry out these three operations at the same time. Some growers, after the first two or three raffia ties, use galvanised wire split-rings for this purpose, and certainly they considerably reduce the time spent on tying and can be used for many seasons. The blooms should be cut regularly, in fact, whether the cordon system or the ordinary method is being used. Never allow blooms to fade and droop on the plants or to form seed-pods, since this will drastically shorten the flowering period.

Advice is given a little later on spraying to keep greenfly in check; but syringing the plants with a "mist" nozzle syringe and clean soft water is sometimes beneficial. But only syringe in warm, settled weather (not during cold spells), either in the early morning after cutting the blooms or, better still, in the evening, when the sun has gone down. In some cases foliar feeding is beneficial, since Sweet Peas, like other plants, can take in nourishment through their leaves. But I am rather dubious about recommending this to a beginner. Unless one has some experience of foliar feeding, the risk of damaging the plants is considerable. However, a liquid seaweed fertiliser like "Maxicrop" would be reasonably safe. This is harmless and can be given every ten to fourteen days if the plants appear to need this extra help. The rate of dilution should not exceed five teaspoonfuls of Maxicrop to 1 gallon of water, applied with a fine rose can or a syringe. Phostrogen too is safe and good. As when syringing with clean water, foliar feeding is best carried out in warm, settled weather and in the evening.

Sweet Pea plants are by no means useless by the time they reach the top of the canes, and nowadays all exhibitors lower or drop them at a convenient period when they are about four feet high. "Dropping" can take place even before the plants reach this height, but allowing at least sixteen days' interval before a show. Lowering is much more simple than it sounds. It is usually, and somewhat misleadingly, called "layering". Commence operations at one end of an outside row by unfastening all ties on the first four to six plants and laying them out on the surface of the ground at an angle to the row, so that they are less liable to be trodden on and damaged. Then, taking great care not to break the haulm, lay the next plant along the ground close up to the canes and gently bend its top twelve to fifteen inches up to the first cane in the row, fastening this top part with two or three raffia ties. Always bear in mind that the top twelve inches or more of the plant are very brittle and easily broken. Make a gradual, not a sharp or "hairpin" bend lower down the haulm, starting the bend at ground level. Then the next plant is fastened likewise to the second cane and so on until the end of the row is reached. The first few plants in the next row are brought round to take the places of the last plants of the previous row and the first plants of the first row then go into position on the last canes of the second row. I know this sounds complicated but it is surprising how easy this operation really is in practice. At first the beginner will be fearful of cracking or breaking the haulm, but after the first few plants have been lowered successfully, he will become more confident. When the operation is finished, the tops of the plants will be little more than a foot above the ground. For the sake of appearance, try to keep the plants at about the same height and tie in any of the haulm which may bulge outwards. If it does not matter being without the flowers for about fourteen days, there is an easier and quicker method of "layering" cordon-grown plants. First remove all flower buds, then unfasten all ties on the plants one by one, and lay them close up to the canes in the manner already described. After a very few days, the heads of the plants will have started to grow upwards and each can then be tied to the nearest cane. This method has the added advantages of giving the plants a substantial rest from flowering and of eliminating all risk of breaking their haulm. This process of lowering can of course be repeated once

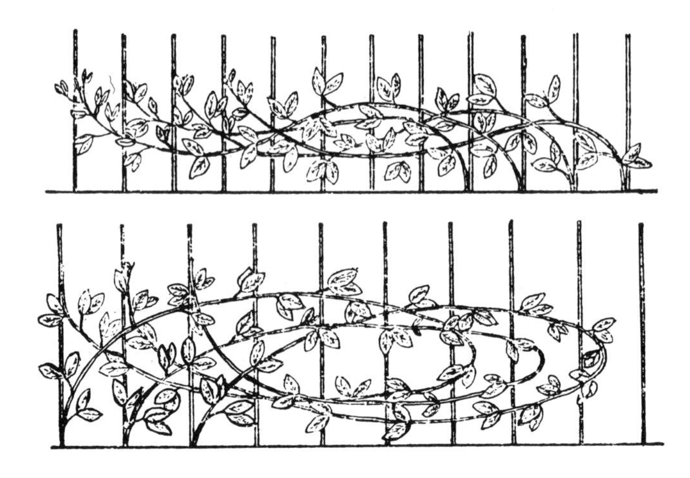

or twice in the season if necessary. Far from harming the plants, this dropping process usually, and rather surprisingly, improves the quality of the blooms produced afterwards.

As far as pests and diseases are concerned, the grower of Sweet Peas has little to fear, comparatively speaking. There are a few contingencies which should be borne in mind, but I must emphasise that the attention I shall now give them *is out of all proportion to their actual importance.*

Diseases. If the plants are kept healthy and free from greenfly then the chance of them contracting any disease is extremely unlikely. "Prevention is better than cure." If a plant or two starts to die, with leaves turning yellow and then brown, it may be a soil pest at its base; it may be "leaf-scorch", or one or more of the virus diseases affecting Sweet Peas which are generally referred to under the names streak and mosaic, the symptoms of which are different. With streak the lower leaves are first affected and become streaked with brownish-black marks and blotches, the discoloration gradually moving up the plant. Mosaic behaves in the opposite way, the top leaves first becoming veined and marbled with yellow. In both, the young growth at the top of the plant becomes stunted and distorted. There may be only one form of mosaic, but probably there are two or more virus diseases to which we refer as "streak". We still have a lot to learn in this connection. If the head of the plant thickens, becomes stunted, malformed and what we term "buzzleheaded", it is certainly either a virus disease or the result of a very bad attack of greenfly. Plants showing any of these symptoms should be pulled up and burnt immediately, for to the best of my belief, *they cannot be cured.* Virus diseases are usually spread by the transmission of contaminated sap by insects, almost always by greenfly. Some growers believe that contaminated sap may be carried from diseased to healthy plants via knives, scissors and even finger nails. Whilst this is quite possible, I think the risk very slight, provided diseased plants are destroyed immediately they are noticed. Most probably leaf-scorch is not a disease at all, but is caused by the respiratory or "digestive" systems of the plant becoming unbalanced. It has been established beyond question that the tendency towards leaf-scorch is much more marked in some varieties and on some soils than on others. At present there is no known cure and no known preventive measures can be adopted. Leaf-scorch seems to be found more frequently below the Midlands than in the North, though in many districts all over the country it is almost unknown, and there is evidence that it is decreasing quite appreciably everywhere. Apart from all this, occasionally cordon-grown plants will die simply as a direct result of the unnatural cordon system itself. They are much more likely to be "thrown off their balance" by wrong and unbalanced feeding agents, bad drainage, or even adverse weather conditions, than plants which are grown naturally. Indeed, diseases and leaf-scorch very rarely affect plants grown in a natural unrestricted manner, but are almost entirely confined to cordon-grown plants. This constitutes a liability and a handicap to the cordon grower which he must grin and bear, through interference with natural growth in order to produce larger blooms on longer stems.

Bud-dropping. This is not a disease at all, only an aggravating phase which, more often than not, passes quickly. Some or all of the buds turn yellow and drop before opening, usually when quite small. Too much moisture at the roots, over-watering, over-feeding, too little sun, abnormally cold or changeable weather; all these, separately or combined, can encourage bud-dropping. Little can be done beyond waiting for it to pass, except of course to withhold watering and feeding for the time being. Cordon plants are much more prone to drop their buds than plants grown naturally and it is most disheartening to the exhibitor when it occurs just before an important show. In spite of the general idea that some varieties are especially liable to drop their buds, I think we should take a more cautious view. With bud-dropping, the pattern of behaviour of the different varieties is irregular and unpredictable, varying from season to season and from garden to garden. Nor do I agree with the widespread opinion among exhibitors that modern varieties are more susceptible to bud-drop than their predecessors. I think that a review of the summer weather over a period of preceding years would suggest a more accurate answer.

Mice. These pests are only troublesome at seed-sowing time. Break-back traps are the remedy as explained previously. Do not roll the seed in red-lead, soak in paraffin, or adopt any other equally dubious method.

Slugs and snails. Again, these attack only very young plants. Any good proprietary slug killer or the well-known Metaldehyde and Bran formula are most effective.

Birds. Netting or strands of black cotton suspended over seedling plants usually check birds. Of late years sparrows have become a menace, taking the young seedlings immediately they come through the soil in pots. I have found a light wooden framework covered with small-mesh wire netting very effective, fitted over cold frames. I still know of no really effective means of stopping tits when they start mutilating flower buds. I am told that anything artificial which looks something like a hawk suspended well above the plants will frighten off tits, but this I have luckily had no need to try. Very few growers ever experience this nuisance.

Wireworms and other soil pests. Any good soil fumigant will shift these; but as usually only an odd plant here and there is affected, the old remedy of potato or carrot "traps" is almost invariably sufficient. These traps consist of pieces of carrot or potato stuck on sticks and buried two or three inches below the surface in positions where wireworms are suspected. Examine the traps each day and kill the wireworms embedded in them.

Greenfly or aphis. The aphis is Public Enemy Number One of the Sweet Pea exhibitor. At best, greenfly sap the vitality of the plants and cause the colours of the flowers to "run" and become distorted. At worst, they spread disease to a much greater extent than all other factors put together. Their attacks are subtle, and the results of those attacks often have the sort of delayed-action effect which throws suspicion away from the real culprits. Knowing this, some growers take the rather drastic precaution of spraying the plants with insecticide throughout their life, at intervals, from the time they are three or four inches high, but not during frosty spells. Administered from a can with a fine rose every three weeks, it provides a sure protection throughout the season. There are quite a number of safe and effective insecticides available (I use Sprayday), but whichever one is used, I strongly advise rigid adherence to the maker's instructions and thorough spraying under the leaves as well as on top of them. Do not wait until a number of greenfly are seen on the plants, but nip the trouble "in the bud" before damage is done. It is perhaps hardly necessary for me to add that if the greenfly are kept in check on roses and other plants in the garden it will help considerably.

Blindness. Occasionally, a leader (on cordon-grown plants) will peter out and come to a blind or dead end, in which case a side or axil growth should be retained to take its place. It is possible to get "caught out" the first time or two and pinch out the last remaining side shoot before noticing that the plant is going blind; but experience will quickly enable the grower to recognise the "thin" appearance of a blind head in good time. The cause of blindness is still obscure, but it may well be the result of a check to growth – frost for example – sustained at a much earlier period than when the blindness becomes apparent. With plants grown naturally blindness is no handicap, for new growths quickly replace any growth that peters out.

When it comes to exhibiting Sweet Peas, there is much that could be written, but I will try to give the essentials. Firstly, the blooms must be cut so that they will be at their best when judged. They must be got to the show without damage and staged in such a manner as to enhance all their good points. That really is a "nutshell" answer and one I really need to explain more fully. Now about cutting: early morning is the best time, usually on the day before a show. This gives the blooms at least twenty-four hours to "fill out" in water. Cut them with the top bud rather more than half-open, or at about that stage of development, for weather conditions may make it advisable to cut at a slightly younger or slightly older stage. Whether you leave them in a cool, heavily shaded place in water after cutting to "keep them back", or place them in the warmth and light of a greenhouse to "bring them on", again depends on the weather, and also on the stage at which they have been cut. Of course, the blooms are best cut when dry, but occasionally no other course is open but to cut them when a heavy dew or rain has left the petals wet. Under such conditions, immediately after cutting, take them in handfuls of 18 to 24 spikes, hold them firmly at the base of their stems and, with a downward movement of the hand (like swatting a fly) "swish" as much water off them as possible. Then stand the spikes somewhere under cover where they are in a strong draught and they will soon dry off. If it is difficult to find a draughty position, use an electric fan. Never pack them while they are damp. How they are taken or sent to the show will be decided by circumstance and convenience; but most exhibitors, after wiping the stems quite dry with a cloth, lay the spikes flat, in layers, in the ordinary florists' cardboard boxes. Often they take the additional precaution of covering the stems themselves with greaseproof paper, for any trace of moisture is liable to mark and disfigure the petals. The great thing is to keep them dry and sufficiently secure to prevent them shaking about and bruising in transit.

Arriving at the show, the very first job should be to get the bunches unfastened and in water, loosely spreading out the heads of the spikes. The usual aid to the arrangement of the spikes in their vases is to fill the vases fairly tightly with thin rushes, cutting these off level with the brim. I much prefer a light arrangement, for I like to be able to see every spike, every flower, without difficulty, and strongly dislike the close "bunched" and over-crowded effect which many exhibitors have adopted in recent years. The Sweet Pea is intrinsically a light, dainty and graceful flower and it "goes against the grain" with me to see these natural attributes disregarded. But, in fairness, I must confess that this is just my personal taste, and it is the judges who have to be pleased. I therefore advise careful note to be taken of the manner in which modern exhibitors arrange their spikes in the vase with mathematical precision and the way they use foliage. Follow their example first. It may be possible, later on, with initiative and courage, to break away from the somewhat formal, "orthodox", but rather monotonous modern ideas of arrangement. Only experience and observation will teach the finer points about exhibiting, though there are one or two obvious details which are often overlooked. All the available spikes of each variety should be examined carefully, and the best selected. By this I mean those which are likely to be at their best *when the judges examine them.* I realise that until experience comes, the problem of deciding which are the best spikes may be difficult.

Mrs Bernard Jones Very successful on the show bench. Raised by Bernard R. Jones

To provide a clear directive to judges and a guide to exhibitors, the National Sweet Pea Society a few years ago drew up a Standard of Perfection, embodied in the following five points, the relative importance of each being in this alphabetical order:

(*a*) Trueness of colour and freshness of bloom.

(*b*) Placement of bloom.

(*c*) Size and form of bloom.

(*d*) Stem proportionate to size of bloom.

(*e*) Effectiveness of staging.

It may help if I add a word or two to explain each of these points. As regards trueness of colour, if a vase of, say, the lavender Leamington is staged, it will probably be disqualified if by accident or design, in addition to Leamington, a spike or spikes of another lavender variety is included. If the schedule states "one variety", "six varieties" or "twelve varieties", that stipulation must be followed exactly. For me, trueness of colour has another meaning. I like to find perfectly natural colouring and would penalise any exhibit where natural colouring has been adversely affected by treatment such as cold storage or too heavy shading. The practice of shading the plants with polythene to protect the blooms from adverse weather is undoubtedly becoming more popular. Protection of some kind or other has been normal procedure for years with exhibitors of several other kinds of flowers and, with our climate, I would not criticise this precaution with Sweet Peas. Freshness counts heavily; see that the bottom bloom on every spike has not started to droop. It is better to use a spike where the top bloom is not fully open than one where the bottom bloom is "tired".

The placement of the blooms on the stem should be even, not gappy. Over-watering, over-feeding, or unbalanced feeding usually results in unsightly gaps between the blooms. Of course, within limits, bad placement can be corrected fairly quickly. If the stems are too long and the blooms gappy, stop pinching out side shoots until good balance is regained. On the other hand, feed and water if the stems are too short and the blooms "bunched" too closely. In the N.S.P.S. Standard of Perfection, neither size and form of bloom nor length of stem are apparently of primary consideration; but they do count heavily and should be in good proportion the one to the other.

"Form" means good form – malformed flowers should be avoided (and by "malformed" I mean that some of the petals are out of proportion or not quite in their proper position). Of late, I am convinced that some judges, including official Trials judges, tend to over-emphasise this fault. My personal opinion is that the odd malformed flower in an exhibit should not be penalised as a major fault and given the same importance by judges as a faded flower. Nor do I consider duplex standards should be regarded as malformed flowers unless they themselves happen to be malformed. It is a matter of personal taste, but as a seedsman I know that most ordinary growers like duplex standards, though many exhibitors do not. I think they tend to enhance appearance, both for exhibition and decoration.

Staging is the last point, but this does not mean that it is unimportant. It not only embodies the arrangement of the spikes in the vases, but also the arrangement of the vases themselves. Place the vases so that their colours do not clash, but rather tend to enhance each other. Effectiveness of staging has a decided bearing on all the other factors, and here experience and close observation of what other exhibitors are doing will help considerably. Count the spikes in each vase *again* before leaving the exhibit and fill each vase to the brim with water just before judging commences. After judging, note carefully where the exhibit has failed (if it has), and if you honestly don't know why your exhibit has been "put down", don't be afraid to ask the judge. It should encourage you to realise that neither you, nor I, nor anyone else will ever finish learning in this delightful, absorbing and wholly fascinating hobby of exhibiting Sweet Peas.

A few words can be said, finally, about those Sweet Pea varieties which are good from an exhibition standpoint. In other countries, the type we know so well here is known as Late Flowering Spencer. This is undoubtedly the best type at present for, broadly speaking, all the others have features which are considered detrimental from a "show-bench" standpoint. Whilst some varieties of Late Spencers are better than others for exhibition, there is no such thing as a *best* half-dozen, dozen, and so on. Ask any twelve successful exhibitors what is their idea of the best dozen varieties, and it is most unlikely that any two of them will exactly agree. In deciding what varieties to grow, it is best at first to stick to the well-tried, reliable and popular exhibition varieties. By the way, I should point out that the varieties which are most popular for the show-bench are somewhat limited in number and in their colour range. Further, some of them are not popular with ordinary growers. Exhibitors tend to avoid some colours altogether. Grow only one or two more varieties than are actually needed. Notice those which appear most frequently in exhibits at better-class Shows

Winning entry for 'The Clay Cup'. The variety is Mrs Bernard Jones.
Courtesy of J.R.F. Bishop

Royal Baby Raised by Rev. T.K. Colledge.

Royal Wedding A top show bench variety of the Spencer type.

and, when finally deciding, vary the colours as much as possible, and avoid growing any two varieties of about the same colouring. In this connection, a most useful guide exists in the Audit of Varieties of Sweet Peas exhibited at the National Sweet Pea Society's Shows which, each year, gives the total number of vases exhibited of each variety, together with the prizes won. It is a very reliable guide to the comparative popularity of the "fashionable" exhibition varieties and is published in the Annual of the Society. This is a very interesting and valuable book, free to members. Incidentally, in my opinion, it would be greatly to the beginner's advantage as an exhibitor to join the National Sweet Pea Society, an organisation which really does further the best interests of Sweet Pea exhibitors. Full particulars will be given on request by the N.S.P.S. Secretary: L. H. O. Williams, Acacia Cottage, Down Ampney, Nr. Cirencester, Glos. GL7 5QW.

Readers may find the following list a useful guide to varieties which are good for exhibition and decoration. I realise that after a few years any such list will be out of date; but those varieties mentioned below are highly regarded at present for exhibition as well as for garden and home decoration.

Blue. Duchess of Roxburghe, Blue Danube, Evensong.

Purple. Royalist, Eclipse.

Mauve. The Doctor, Pall Mall.

Maroon. Milestone, Black Prince, Midnight, Joker.

Cerise, orange and salmon shades. Diana, Brian Clough, Frances Perry Improved, Sheila Macqueen, Sunsilk, Herald.

Rose and carmine. Dynasty, Lustre, Corinne.

Scarlet, orange-scarlet and orange shades. Red Arrow, Our Joyce, Blaze, Troubadour.

White. Royal Wedding, White Leamington, Captain Scott.

Cream. Cream Southbourne, Margot.

Pink on cream ground. Charles Unwin, Terry Wogan, Fiona.

Pink on white ground. Sally Unwin, Catherine, Southbourne, Mrs. Bernard Jones, Pink Bouquet.

Flushed. Lady Fairbairn, Percy Thrower, Champagne Bubbles, Honeymoon.

Picotee. Rosy Frills, Ballerina, Topsy.

Crimson. Gipsy Queen, Winston Churchill.

Lavender. Royal Baby, Southampton, Leamington.

CHAPTER V

ORDINARY CULTURAL METHODS

There will no doubt be many readers of these pages who want reasonably good blooms for cutting, but cannot afford the time and trouble which exhibition culture demands. It will help them considerably if they ignore or forget most of the cultural details given on previous pages! In spite of whatever may have been heard or read to the contrary, in spite of whatever ideas may already have been circulated about Sweet Pea culture, the fact remains that really good blooms for cutting and garden display can be produced with no more trouble than it takes to grow Culinary Peas. The public image of the flower has changed drastically since the discovery of the cordon method of growing. Constant publicity, given over the years to the innumerable details and intricacies of cordon management, is responsible for the completely fallacious, but very widespread public impression that Sweet Peas are difficult, time absorbing and fastidious. In fact, their culture only *becomes* difficult when they are grown by the elaborate and exacting cordon method. The bare essentials of ordinary culture can be given in one short sentence. Sow (or plant) them, give them supports to climb, an occasional hoeing to check the weeds and then let them go their own sweet way without interference. Actually, they resent being pampered and "fussed". However, though they can be grown simply and easily, no other flower will produce a greater reward for a little extra care and forethought.

Just as with cordon culture, I advise readers to buy the best quality seeds, following their own colour tastes and requirements in respect to types and varieties. Sowing times and methods remain the same as for exhibition culture, but soil preparation need not be nearly as elaborate as for cordon-grown plants. If the ground is just dug over and manure is turned in, as for any ordinary vegetable crop, ample supplies of cut blooms may be confidently expected all through summer and early autumn. Deeper digging, such as double digging, and a little more manure, will usually bring rather better results and for a little longer period.

Sweet Peas growing naturally up cane supports.
Courtesy of Practical Gardening

Sweet Pea seedlings planted out with posts in position ready for supporting wire.

When it comes to planting out, some positions and circumstances make clumps or rings twelve to eighteen inches in diameter an attractive proposition, and such clumps, on sticks or netting supports, can be very effective indeed. Most people plant a row, or rows, usually in the vegetable garden, for cut flowers rather than for garden decoration. Single rows are more practical than double rows, and the plants may be given less space in the rows than for exhibition, four to six inches apart, or even two plants together, six inches between each pair. For the tall-growing types, sticks or branches about six feet high as for culinary peas, make convenient and natural-looking supports. Wire netting and twine are both satisfactory, though both need supporting with poles, posts or stout bamboo canes. Then there are many other ways in which supports can be improvised: netting fastened to a fence or wall, string stretched between the posts of a pergola, a few sticks against an old tree stump, and so on. Planting out should be done at the same time and in the same way as for cordons, but apart from removing the first flower buds to allow the plants to gain strength, no restriction of growth should be practised. *Faded flower spikes must be removed regularly.* It will shorten the flowering period and check vigorous growth if seed pods are permitted to form.

To keep up vigorous growth and prolong the time over which good spikes may be cut, mulching, feeding and watering on the lines already mentioned may be carried out if the necessary time is available. Greenfly must be kept in check. When I was a boy, Sweet Pea culture was perfectly simple, for they were treated as ordinary hardy annuals. Indeed, most people in the southern half of England sowed them outdoors in late September or early October. The seed was very cheap then and sowing was rather thick, an ounce (about 300 seeds) to eight or nine yards of row; but in nine seasons out of ten they pulled through the winter without protection and gave a magnificent show. *Sweet Peas are still hardy annuals and can still safely be treated as such.*

CHAPTER VI

INDOOR DECORATION

It is quite unnecessary to attempt to extol the value of Sweet Peas as cut flowers. By day, and by artificial light, their extreme diversity of charming colours, their brightness, the ease with which they can be arranged, their delightful fragrance, and their adaptability to any and every kind of decoration, are qualities which have been largely instrumental in raising the Sweet Pea to its present unrivalled position in popular esteem. The great advantage of being able to cut and cut again in almost all weather conditions throughout the summer, and well into the autumn, make them beloved by all who appreciate the quiet cheerfulness they broadcast in the home. It is difficult indeed to place Sweet Peas in any kind of vase in such a way as to render them unsightly. Take a handful of spikes as cut, place the bunch straight into a vase, and the result will be quite pleasing. So much so, that one fears this is the rule rather than the exception in most households. On the other hand, there are few flowers which so amply repay one for a little more care in their arrangement than this somewhat lazy treatment, a little more consideration in the choice of vases, colours, and foliages. I make no personal claim to excel in the arrangement of flowers, yet through long association with Sweet Peas, a keen appreciation of their enhanced beauty when nicely arranged, a perpetual itch to experiment with different arrangements and colours, and the experience acquired by judging and noting with great interest the decorative classes at Flower Shows, I could hardly avoid learning something of how they may be arranged to best advantage.

It is not a bad plan to endeavour to follow Nature's own decorative effects when arranging almost all kinds of cut flowers. Those which we think most pleasing when massed together will usually be found growing and flowering in a mass. But the Sweet Pea, which appears at its very best when treated lightly, grows naturally in a dainty, graceful manner, its blooms poised in the air around the plant, like coloured butterflies. This, then, is my first and certainly most important word of advice: study the general effect given by a row or clump of Sweet

Pink Bouquet A variety with well spaced flowers on long stems. Raised by F.C. Harriss.

Peas when in full bloom. Study plants that have been grown naturally and not on the cordon system, and endeavour to reproduce that same light, airy appearance in your vases or bowls. There should be just enough blooms to make a fairly substantial impression of colour or colours, but not crowded to an extent which confines the entire beauty of decoration to colour only. There is usually a general tendency to overcrowd the flowers, and rarely does one notice full advantage being taken of the increased charm imparted by a fairly lavish use of foliage and buds. Sweet Peas are anything but stiff and formal when growing. They do not conform to any design or pattern like slats on a fence, or soldiers on parade. Therefore, any attempt to place them in alignment in a vase in a similar manner to the section of a wheel, with the spokes for stems, is far too formal. I do not mean to imply that the decoration should be top-heavy or one-sided, but it is possible, by varying the height of the stems, and by the use of bent stems, and of flowers and buds cut with a reasonable length of foliage or haulm, to break up a formal outline and avoid any suspicion of stiffness. Do not keep the flowers on the same plane. They look much better at varying heights in the decoration – though this should not be carried to absurd lengths.

Exhibition blooms, with 1½ to 2 feet stems, are always more formal in appearance than the naturally grown spikes, whilst the large leathery foliage from cordons is well-nigh useless from a decorative viewpoint. I do not mean that these large exhibition spikes are any the less useful, but they are just a little more difficult to arrange in a light, dainty manner. However, the fact that it is possible to use them in larger decorative schemes, where eight or nine inch stems would be lost, affords compensation. With Sweet Peas, every flower spike should stand out by itself, and no appreciable crowding should be apparent from whatever side the decoration is viewed. It is always wise to arrange vases from the particular angle at which they will eventually be seen. For example, if vases are to occupy a high position, such as a mantelpiece or the top of a sideboard, do not first arrange them on a low table, or most probably when they are lifted up they will not appear nearly as effective as they did when looked at from above. Stems are normally only slightly curved, and in almost every decoration it is necessary to give some of the stems a much more decided bend. This is quite simple. Take an ordinary straight stem, and pull it slowly through the first finger and thumb of the left hand, exerting a fairly firm pressure, at the same time gently bending it to the desired position with the right hand. Do this several times, on each occasion bending the stem a little further until it conforms with one's requirements. In this way the use of florist's wire can be dispensed with, and if necessary a sufficient bend can be imparted so as to leave the flowers facing upwards instead of to the side, without actually breaking the stem or injuring it in any way. As a general rule, the highest point of the decoration should be foliage rather than a flower, and if the apex is a little to one side of the centre of the decoration, so much the better from an artistic point of view.

Some readers may wonder when is the best time to cut the flowers for indoor decoration. Actually, cutting may be carried out at any time of the day, but I prefer the early morning or late evening. Use a very sharp pair of scissors, or preferably a penknife, and cut the spikes with as long stems as is possible – they can be shortened later if desired. Place them in water immediately, and if possible allow them to stand there for a few hours before arranging them. Many colours, especially the delicate shades, lose a little of their richness when the sun has been shining on them for a few hours. Admittedly they will "fill in", as it is termed, to a large extent in water, but not quite to the same degree as when they are cut in the early morning. As in cutting for exhibition, avoid all spikes which are fully open, or the bottom flower will droop within a few hours. It is better to cut when the top bloom is still in the bud stage, or just beginning to expand. I like to cut a small proportion at a still younger stage, but my preference for at least a few buds in any Sweet Pea decorations is purely personal. Some colour tones, such as the crimsons, mauves, deep and medium blues, purples, carmines, maroons, and the deep rose shades, lose some of their brightness when cut, if only in a very small degree. On the other hand, almost all the lavenders seem to take on a purer, softer tone in water, whilst the orange and salmon tones become slightly richer. Many of the pinks, flushes, cream pinks and cerises have a cleaner if slightly lighter appearance, and on the whole most colours improve after a few hours in water.

The choice of vases or other receptacles is largely a matter for taste and circumstances to decide. Vases should be slender, not heavy-looking or with a large base, and not highly coloured. Plain glass or silverware is excellent, while the rustic-ware tubular table centres and side pieces impart a natural and very graceful appearance, and lend themselves to easy and quick arrangement.

I have seen many exquisitely arranged silver, glass and black rose bowls but, on the whole, unless one has a light touch, they are apt to look slightly heavy and dumpy. Where colour effect alone is required, they will be found ideal, and the long-stemmed exhibition blooms, which are themselves rather heavy and massive, are more effective in bowls than those grown in the ordinary way. Exhibition blooms, too, are very suitable for an ornamental basket in the hall, fireplace, or a small table in the corner of a room.

When using opaque bowls or vases with fairly wide tops, it is advisable to have some method of support for the stems, otherwise they are liable to fall to the bottom. Rose bowls usually have a wire or glass support to facilitate arrangement, but if silver sand (washed quite clean) is put into them within an inch or two of the top, it will be found more effective, especially with very low bowls. The sand should be washed every time it is used to keep it sweet. A good method with opaque vases is to push thin rushes, straw, or thick stems of grass into them, cutting it off level with scissors at the brim. This allows a much quicker and easier arrangement, and full advantage can be taken of the length of stems, which only need inserting about half an inch. The disadvantage of this method lies in the necessity for filling up with water more frequently. I need hardly mention the advisability of keeping the inside of vases and bowls clean by frequent washing out.

As regards foliage, I prefer the Sweet Pea foliage itself, with its shapely leaves and curly tendrils, and perhaps a few of the feathery flowering shoots of the pretty wild grasses to be found in any ditch or hedgerow. One particular kind of wild grass (I do not know its botanical name) is a great favourite of mine, and is almost smoke-like in its extreme lightness. When the thin, slender lateral growths of Sweet Pea plants are cut with an open spike and a bud or two just colouring, no more effective foliage can be obtained, and it should be used freely. Most retail seed firms, including Unwins, list a comprehensive range of kinds of ornamental grasses which can be used to suit the taste of the arranger.

I have a purely personal dislike of Gypsophila, perhaps due to the frequency with which one observes its use. It is not unsightly, of course, or it would never be so popular; but if I had to use Gypsophila it would be in a very sparing manner. The two well-known kinds of indoor Asparagus – Plumosus and Sprengeri – are much more to be preferred, or even the feathery fronds of the culinary kind. Where trailing or "weeping" foliage is required, some of the fine-leaved reddish-brown and silver-brown greenhouse trailing plants with hanging foliage are excellent, or where these are unobtainable, the young growths of Ampelopsis Veitchii, Selaginella, the young tinted leaves of Berberis, and the foliage of Clematis and the wild "Red Robin" are also effective. Smilax, too, may be used in large and ambitious decorations.

The judicious choice of varieties or colours of flowers is one of the most important points in all floral decorative work. With Sweet Peas one has such a wonderfully diverse range from which to select – colours and colour combinations are to be found to suit all tastes and all occasions. To some, it matters little what shades are mixed in a vase or bowl – all are beautiful. Others with a more acute colour sense are very critical; a decorative scheme, in which the colours clash, jars on them to an extent that is hardly credible. Let me make this perfectly clear by means of a musical illustration. If one strikes the keys of a piano in a haphazard way, an unpleasantly jarring discord is made, but if one strikes notes which are in harmony, there is a beautiful blending of sound. The various colours and shades in flowers are very similar to the tones and half tones in music; taking them singly they are all more or less equally beautiful, but mix them up and it is possible to create an harmonious blending or a discordant effect. Generally speaking our eye for colour is not so well developed as our ear for music; yet there are few who will not express appreciation of the harmony of a well chosen colour blending, although they may only vaguely recognise it as such.

Excellent effects can be produced by using one variety or colour only in a vase or decorative scheme, and here choice will be purely and simply a matter of personal taste. The lighter shades appear at their best in daylight. Light lavenders, pale blues, pale pinks, cream-pinks or soft flushes, lose much of the delicate colouring, which is their chief asset, under artificial light. On the other hand, the deeper colours which by daylight may appear slightly harsh, brighten by artificial light, particularly if a few creams or whites are intermixed. Almost all colours with a fair amount of orange or salmon in their composition look particularly well under artificial light. The background of the decoration, the prevailing colours of the room furnishings, and even the state of the weather, all have their bearing on the effect produced. On a hot day, a cool effect would be produced by blending white and lavender, while in colder weather a blending of orange and cream would strike a decidedly warmer note. I must say the warm tones attract me more than the colder ones, and I believe this preference to be general.

The following are suggestions of two-colour combinations which reflect my personal taste. No particular varieties, but colour tones only are given:

Cream or light cream-pink with orange, salmon, orange-scarlet, orange-cerise, or lavender.

Pure white with almost any colours and shades that are not on cream grounds.

Light blue or lavender with orange, salmon, or salmon-cerise.

Pale pink blushes or flushes on white grounds with light lavenders or lavender-blues.

One could go on with such suggestions, for there is no end to the number of pleasing combinations which can be found by experiment.

A good deal of care must be exercised in combining three or more colours in a decoration. It is advisable, when three are used, to include a few only of whichever colour is the most decided contrast to the other two, and to keep them towards the bottom part of the decoration rather than the top. The following will be found effective:

White and pale pink with a few red, orange, or even purple or maroon.

Cream, light cream-pink with a few orange, salmon, cerise or purple.

Cream, salmon-cream-pink with a few bright orange or orange-scarlet. This is one of my favourite combinations, especially if a little rich "autumn" tinted foliage is used, and it is equally effective by day or by artificial light.

Varieties which lose their brightness in water or which take on a harsher tone when cut a few hours should be avoided, and also those which are difficult to blend with others.

Quite apart from the pleasure a beautiful arrangement gives to others, there is a great deal of enjoyment and satisfaction to be derived in the process of making it. Time spent in artistically arranging flowers is never wasted and always appreciated. Some folks are, most fortunately, gifted with good taste for the work; but experience will improve all, and one must experiment with different combinations of colours, foliage and arrangements, for practice alone makes perfect in this, as in many other arts.

CHAPTER VII

COLD GREENHOUSE CULTURE

Because I am sure this phase of Sweet Pea culture will only be possible for comparatively few of my readers, I do not intend to take up a great deal of space with minor details, but will give the main cultural points briefly, more especially for those who have a cold greenhouse and who wish to grow early blooms. For many, early blooms have a great fascination, and of late years market growers have found under-glass flowers quite profitable. Large and fairly high structures, devoted wholly to Sweet Peas, are best for the purpose; but not many amateur growers have such facilities. Where a suitable greenhouse is available, the owner – nine times out of ten – will not feel disposed to give space to Sweet Peas, but will prefer to grow subjects which are less suitable for outdoor culture.

Anyone who has seen good quality blooms grown on the exhibition or cordon system indoors, cannot have failed to notice their wonderfully clean appearance, and the beautifully clear, soft shades of some of the varieties, as compared with outdoor grown flowers. Most of the specialist firms used to grow and exhibit indoor blooms, but few amateurs are likely to devote much greenhouse space to their culture. There are many advantages to be obtained from indoor culture, amongst them being the comparative absence of disease, and the greater control which the grower has over the plants. Plastic covered structures are as effective and much less expensive than a cold greenhouse.

Cold greenhouse treatment varies little from outdoor culture, whether one intends to practise the cordon system or just to grow them naturally for decorative purposes. One may use large pots, or better still – but not always practicable – fairly shallow trenches in the ground of the greenhouse. Early autumn sowing in pots or boxes gives best results and planting should be done about a fortnight earlier than if the plants were intended for outside cultivation, though exactly the same hardy treatment is essential. Keep the plants in their cold frames until mid-January, and then bring the pots or boxes into the greenhouse; but do not transplant for a fortnight, so as to enable the plants to become acclimatised to their new situation.

It is often necessary, when growing plants in the soil of the greenhouse, to remove part of the old and bring in some new soil from the garden. This gives one the opportunity of mixing in decayed leaf mould or the remains of an old hot-bed. Elaborate trenching is quite unnecessary, and if the trenches are made two spits deep and two feet wide, this will be found ample, even if blooms of exhibition quality are one's object. Follow the same methods in soil preparation as advised in earlier pages, breaking up the bottom roughly to allow adequate drainage, and well mixing into the lower spit a fair dressing of decayed horse or farmyard manure, bone meal and soot. The animal manure should not be brought nearer the surface than about nine inches, but a little Phostrogen, bone meal, or compost in the top layer will help. A firm soil is very necessary, and since the trenched ground under glass will not naturally sink as firm as the outdoor soil, this should be trodden well down when it is prepared, unless it is in a wet, sticky condition, in which case allow the soil to dry off before pressing down. Finish the preparation of the trenches before Christmas, and give a good watering once or twice, according to soil conditions. Water again a few days before transplanting the seedlings, when the earth should be nicely moist all through. Space is limited, and the rows need not be as far apart as in outdoor culture. A three foot path is sufficient between single and double rows, allowing a foot between double rows.

When planting in pots, good fibrous loam with a little bone meal and wood ash mixed in should be used as the potting medium; but no animal manure should be incorporated unless it is well decayed. It is better to let the roots find their way out through the drainage hole into a fairly richly prepared bed of decayed manure and loam (or leaf mould) on which the pots can be stood. The hole in the pot bottoms may be enlarged specially for this purpose. Make the potting soil very firm when transplanting the seedlings, and allow space at the top for top dressing later. The planting of seedlings, whether in pots or trenches, should be done during early February. Always select the strongest and healthiest plants, for it is unwise to give up valuable greenhouse space to weak or spindly specimens. Space them four to six inches apart if in rows, or one plant to a six or seven inch, and three to a ten or twelve inch pot. Plant firmly in the same way as advised for exhibition culture outdoors, and do not water too freely at first. Just keep the soil nicely moist until strong growth commences.

Support the plants with short twigs, and give them plenty of fresh air. At all stages grow them as coolly as possible, and do not attempt to force growth by heat. Sudden changes of temperature are detrimental, but by opening the ventilators to their fullest extent on warm days, and closing down towards evening, a fairly even temperature can be maintained. In the early summer, whitening sprayed on the glass will tend to keep the inside temperature low.

As the plants will not be blown about by the wind, the method of supporting them need not be so heavy as for outdoor growth. Wide mesh cord netting is ideal and very neat, even for cordon-grown plants, or stout strands of string or binder-twine tied vertically, six inches apart, on two or three horizontal wires, are also serviceable and economical, and will take the place of bamboos quite satisfactorily. When growing on the cordon system, follow the same procedure as for outdoors, restricting each plant to one or – at the most – two leaders, pinching out laterals and tendrils, and fastening with raffia or wire rings to the netting. When vertical strings are used, these can be tied fairly loosely to the two horizontal wires, and the plants twisted round as they grow. This is the method often used for supporting tomato plants, and it is quick and effective. Allow the plants to become well established, and to make a growth of a foot or fifteen inches before starting to restrict them to one or two leaders.

As soon as the plants begin to flower, apply a top dressing of loose horse litter around their base, and if they appear to need further assistance, begin to feed with liquid animal manure and soot water, but be careful not to over-feed, more particularly at first. Do not attempt to make use of chemical fertilisers unless you have experience, although after the flowers have been in bloom for a few weeks, a stimulant now and again – such as nitrate of soda or nitrate of potash (half an ounce to the gallon of water) – may be beneficial if applied at the right time. With plants in full bloom in trenches, a good watering will be necessary once every five or six days, according to the nature of the soil and temperature. Those in pots should be watered a little more frequently. On warm evenings occasionally syringe the foliage of the plants with soft water that has stood in the greenhouse for several hours.

When the cordon plants reach the glass, they should be lowered, as advised for outdoor culture. The lowering may be repeated two or three times during the season if necessary according to the height of the house and the length of time the plants are required for cut bloom. The length of haulm will sometimes measure between twenty and thirty feet when this lowering method is followed, and with proper soil treatment.

Plants grown in a natural manner indoors will, of course, furnish a much greater quantity of bloom, but of poorer quality than from cordons, and the foliage in the rows will be wider and more straggling. Netting or strands of string fixed horizontally can be used as supports, and by taking out a few of the laterals in overcrowded places, and training some of the remaining ones horizontally, the plants may be kept somewhat within bounds, and will produce a mass of blooms from top to bottom. When the growths reach the glass in fairly low houses, pinch their tips out to give the laterals a better chance. Be very careful to remove faded flowers, and do not allow seed pods to form, or the flowering season will soon be over. Aphis and mildew are the only pests likely to cause trouble, and these should be checked as soon as they put in an appearance.

It is possible – by sowing the Early or Winter-flowering type from August to early September – to obtain Sweet Pea blooms at Christmas. They need no heat other than just sufficient to keep out frost, and as they flower in about sixteen to eighteen weeks from the time of sowing, and never make such strong growth as the later type, it is best to sow in large pots outdoors, in a cold frame, and move them, without transplanting, well before the winter. Plants of the Winter-flowering type should never be "pinched".

As far as growth and treatment are concerned, all varieties of Sweet Peas are equally good for greenhouse culture. However, it is a fact that some colours are much better than others under glass. With several varieties there is an undoubted improvement in colour, whilst with others exactly the reverse occurs. Those few varieties which need shading from the sun outdoors to preserve their colour, are particularly effective under glass. In fact, in general terms, it would be correct to say that all varieties which have salmon or orange in their colour make-up improve under glass. On the other hand, some of the "hard" colours – particularly those of the deeper hues – are seen at their best outdoors.

CHAPTER VIII

ON VARIETIES

To the would-be exhibitor, the best advice I can give regarding the selection of varieties is this: decide on the number of varieties that are intended for show (i.e. in six-bunch, eight-bunch, twelve-bunch classes, etc.) and only grow two more varieties than are absolutely necessary. For example, if the minimum number of varieties really needed is twelve, do not grow more than fifteen, but grow as many plants of each of these as circumstances allow. The wisdom of this advice will be very apparent when it comes to cutting the exhibition blooms. I have already pointed out that many successful exhibitors sow double the seed of each variety that they really need in plants, thus allowing for germination failures and other losses, and also the opportunity of choosing the best and most sturdy plants when transplanting.

Not the least of the problems which confront the beginner is that of making a satisfactory choice of varieties. There are so many in commerce, and although the merits of the older ones are reasonably well-known, it is the introduction of new ones each year which complicates matters, and the specialist's or seedsman's catalogue does not make the inexperienced amateur's task of choosing varieties much easier. The seedsman may do his level best to explain what the varieties he offers are like, but very few people have identical ideas in respect to the description of colour. One has noted a very popular variety described as "bright orange-cerise", "vivid scarlet", and "brilliant red" in three different catalogues, and another as "lavender-mauve", "deep lavender" and "soft lilac". Of course, it would be reasonably easy to confine one's selection to the well tried general favourites of the more successful exhibitors; but such a course leaves little scope for personal taste, and in consequence would not appeal to all.

Ask ten acknowledged Sweet Pea experts to name what they consider the best twelve varieties in cultivation. Not only will every selection differ, but some also will vary to a considerable extent. In point of fact, *there is no such thing* as a "best" half-dozen, dozen or eighteen. In many colour sections there is no such thing as a "best" variety; it all depends on individual taste and, to a lesser degree, on the slight variations arising from the suitability of some varieties for certain localities. Points of difference between varieties which appear quite insignificant, or even invisible, to the casual observer or inexperienced grower assume larger proportions and greater importance to the enthusiast. Every keen exhibitor enjoys an argument on the merits of the different varieties and in comparing opinions about them with others.

The annual influx of new varieties is, from the exhibitor's standpoint, something of a mixed blessing. He knows full well that he cannot hope to compete with superior varieties, even though they are grown no better than his own, and very naturally wishes to acquire any new introductions which may keep him up-to-date, and perhaps afford even a slight advantage on the show-bench. Yet, if he is experienced, he fully realises the risk he runs of growing too many untried new Sweet Peas. He cannot overlook the fact that a great many of these have, in the past, proved inferior to similar varieties already in commerce. He knows too, that as a rule at least five or six new varieties are introduced each year, but that only a very few will ever attain popularity, whilst less than one in ten is destined to become a general favourite. It is the same with all popular flowers. It is not that the raisers of these new varieties deliberately introduce inferior kinds. Public taste is not easy to assess and, in any case, raisers naturally look upon their own creations – usually the result of many years' hard work – in rather a different light from others. After all, every mother's baby which is entered in a Baby Show is the best in its mother's eyes, no matter what the judges think. The best guide to the merit of a new variety, and to the accuracy of its catalogue description, undoubtedly lies in the reputation of its raiser. To my mind it is all to the good that there are a good many raisers and, in consequence, many new introductions each year, for only in that way can we hope to achieve real progress. Public opinion, in the long run, sifts the wheat from the tares; and in the aggregate it is the exhibitor's judgment – for good or ill – which largely determines the degree of popularity of new Sweet Peas.

There are certain colours and colour sections not greatly favoured by present-day exhibitors for various reasons. It may be that in some there is a liability to "spot" in adverse weather. A few colour sections do not at present contain a single variety of sufficient merit for keen

Pat Mitchell A strong growing variety giving four or more flowers per stem.

competition, even though they may embrace several which are popular for garden and home decoration. Yet again, a few colour sections are avoided for the reason that less difficult or more effective exhibition varieties are found elsewhere. Modern exhibitors rarely stage a maroon, crimson, or deep blue, whilst purples, mid-blues, and even mauves, are not very much more popular. In the main, all these are inclined to "spot", and to lose something of their brightness in water. Stripes are rarely seen on the show bench, but this may be due to the fact that there are few stripes in commerce at the present moment really suitable for cordon growing. But I have at least one new stripe – a great improvement on the old Fantasy – in the "workshop" stage, and I suspect that this picture may change within the next few years.

The beginner who aspires to show bench success would be well advised to restrict his varieties to those which are well-tried and reliable. In this connection the National Sweet Pea Society's *Audit of Varieties*, referred to towards the end of Chapter IV, furnishes an excellent guide for the inexperienced to the comparative popularity of the varieties used by the best exhibitors in the country.

If one's requirements are confined to producing cut flowers for the home, and not the show bench, the problem of what varieties to choose does not arise, for then it is simply a case of giving full rein to one's colour preferences.

Blue Danube The finest deep mid-blue. Raised by Tom Morris.

CHAPTER IX

RAISING NEW VARIETIES

"He who makes two blades of grass grow where only one grew before, is a public benefactor." That statement was made many years ago, but when I first read it I immediately thought of the plant hybridist, who might also, with equal truth, be described as an inventor, even though his "inventions" are not as startling or as obvious as those in many other spheres. Yet, to the human race, the value of new wheats, new fruits or new vegetables, which surpass the older kinds in cropping capacity, flavour, hardiness, immunity from disease, or other desirable qualities, is in the aggregate immense. New and improved flowers may not be of such material benefit to mankind; yet they surely play their part in the sum total of progress. Perhaps we can only estimate their real effect in its true perspective by looking backwards. Gardeners of two hundred years ago, or less, would be astounded if they could but see the improvements which have taken place in the floral world. It is my object in this chapter to review simply, and of necessity briefly, how these improvements have been effected, more particularly with Sweet Peas. Nature has often played her part with a startling leap forward, but in the main, development has been brought about slowly, steadily, and laboriously, as the direct outcome of careful scientific hybridisation and selection by the plant breeder. Scientific plant breeding might almost be described as controlled evolution.

The science of genetics is complex and difficult to grasp; but I see no reason why some of the basic facts should not be conveyed simply, and in unscientific language. In point of fact, my approach to it, like my experience, will be practical rather than scientific. In endeavouring to explain I think it will help if I refer to plants other than Sweet Peas – perhaps even using animals by way of illustration as well as plants.

Plants perpetuate themselves in several widely differing ways, but in raising new varieties we are only concerned with those kinds which can and do reproduce themselves by means of seeds. There is great variation among these, but speaking generally, both male and female organs are present in each individual flower, and again, both are usually ready to function at the same time. The male organs are the stamens, which carry at their end or top the little pollen sacs called anthers, and when these are fully ripe they burst and release the powdery pollen, which in most flowers is yellow or primrose in colour. In using the word "ripe" I mean that the pollen is ready and at the right stage to play its own partricular part in fertilisation. The female part of the flower is contained in one or more pistils, the parts of which are termed stigma, style and ovary. In a Sweet Pea bloom these can be readily distinguished by stripping it of its petals and keel. The stamens will be seen surrounding the pistil, and on close examination the extreme end or stigma will be found slightly sticky, whilst just underneath it is covered with very fine hairs. The style leads direct to the ovary, which is an immature seed pod, containing the undeveloped seeds. Fertilisation with the Sweet Pea is exactly the same as with most other flowers, pistil and stamens being ripe at the same time. Some of the powdery pollen is transferred by contact to the sticky stigma, and to the hairs already mentioned. The pollen grain throws out a kind of tube which pushes through the surface of the stigma, down through the style, into the ovary, where it enters and fertilises one of the ovules or immature seeds. This is admittedly a somewhat rough and ready explanation of the process of fertilisation, but I feel sure most readers will easily grasp what happens in the case of the Sweet Pea.

Ranging over the whole field of flowers, we find Nature adopting various methods of getting the pollen on to the stigma. With the Sweet Pea it is by direct contact; but with some flowers it simply drops on to the stigma by the force of gravity. Often it is carried from flower to flower by the wind, or by insects, and there are several other ways. It will be realised that, unlike most other flowers, the Sweet Pea is naturally self-pollinated or self-fertilised, each flower utilising its own pollen for this function. The two petals which are joined to form the keel cover up and protect the stamens and pistil at the time fertilisation takes place, and there is the further protection afforded by the other petals, for with the Sweet Pea fertilisation takes place *before* the flower is fully open. Here again, an examination of a number of buds just on the point of opening will show the exact stage at which the anthers burst, and it will be seen that the flower is not liable to natural cross-pollination by the wind, insects, or any other agency. This is why it is possible, and indeed the usual method, to grow a large number of varieties of Sweet Peas for seed purposes in the same field, for there is no fear of cross-fertilisation taking place and ruining the trueness of stocks, as would be the case with most other flowers and vegetables. When cross-fertilisation does take place – and this is extremely rare – it is due to the keel being malformed, allowing the pistil to become exposed. Bees and other insects do not cross-fertilise Sweet Peas; they simply suck nectar from the base of the blooms.

Assuming that the process of self-fertilisation has been understood, we now pass on to cross-fertilisation. This term simply means the fertilisation of one variety by the pollen of another, and the artificial cross-fertilisation of any flower implies the removal of its own anthers before they shed their pollen, and the transference of pollen from another variety to its pistil, taking due precautions against pollen from any other source reaching the pistil while it is still potent.

From these general observations we return to the Sweet Pea, which we have seen is self-fertilised if left to its own devices. My own method of crossing is simple – a bud is selected on the point of opening and holding it gently but firmly in the left hand the standard and wing on the left-hand side are folded back and held in that position by the fingers. Then with a small pair of pointed tweezers or forceps (a needle would do just as well) the keel is cut in two from bottom to top, thus exposing the anthers and pistil. Care should be duly exercised so as not to injure the pistil in any way. It will immediately be seen whether the anthers have burst and released any pollen, and if so, one immediately starts operations on another slightly younger flower. With a little practice the right selection of buds is almost automatic.

The next operation is the removal of all stamens with the tweezers, again taking care not to puncture or injure the pistil. The flower which we are making the female parent of the cross has thus been emasculated. Now pick a half-open bloom of whatever variety you have chosen as the male or pollen parent. The keel can be gently pulled down to expose the stamens and pistil, or it can be given a slight pull and completely removed. It is then easy to transfer the ripe pollen on to the stigma of the female parent by contact, or by the aid of a small fine-haired brush. I never use a brush for Sweet Peas, for actual contact is easy and quick, whereas the brush method is somewhat wasteful of pollen, and the brush must be thoroughly cleaned up before the pollen of another variety can be used.

It might be thought that since the pollen of the bud we have made the female was not ripe at the time the cross was made the female parts might be too young, but in practice I have found that there are several hours latitude in either direction. A successful cross made in the manner I have described is just as likely as if one had waited a day after emasculating before pollinating the flower. Ripe pollen may be kept alive for two or three days if necessary, and will remain "alive" or potent; but it starts to function almost immediately if it is transferred to a stigma. On occasion I have used a small tin box or glass tube to store pollen for a day or two, but have not carried out experiments to determine either the period it will remain potent, or the best method of storing it. Indeed, storing is only necessary in cases where there are not sufficient buds available on the female parent at the time and one has been forced to wait. In theory, any buds of the right age on a Sweet Pea stem are equally suitable for crossing. But in practice I always prefer to make the first or oldest bud on any stem the female parent. Very often it is possible to cross the first two buds on the stem at the same time. Of course, the remaining buds on the stem should be nipped off, and a small label attached to the stem bearing the number of the cross, for in plant breeding exact records should always be taken and retained, year after year. With many other flowers it is quite necessary, after crossing, to protect the seed or female parent from natural cross-fertilisation by wind or insects. Usually a grease-proof paper bag is chosen for this purpose. But with Sweet Peas I have never found protection necessary, for "foreign" pollen is extremely unlikely to interfere with one's work.

Though the actual operation of crossing Sweet Peas is simple, and can be practised by anyone sufficiently interested, some judgment must be exercised as to when the crosses are made, in order to obtain seed pods. A spell of fine, sunshiny weather during the first three weeks in July provides the right circumstances with autumn-sown, outdoor-grown plants, and from mid-July to mid-August for spring-sown plants – though only in exceptional seasons will spring-sown plants set seed as freely as autumn-sown, and the hybridist would be well advised to operate only with autumn-sown. In parts of the country where Sweet Peas rarely produce seedpods outdoors it is necessary to rely on greenhouse-grown plants for hybridisation.

Perhaps it is advisable to mention here that no visible change takes place in the actual bloom that has been artificially or naturally cross-fertilised. One has to await succeeding generations for whatever changes are coming. Again I would emphasise that crossing the Sweet Pea, though simple, should be done delicately, with a minimum of injury or bruising to buds and flower stem. After crossing, one simply awaits the ripening of whatever seed pods are formed. These are then

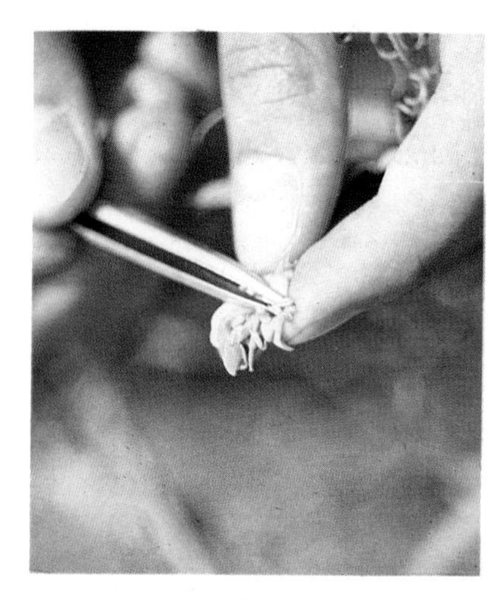

Opening a flower bud prior to cross-fertilisation.

Removal of stamens before transferring selected pollen from another plant.

carefully gathered, and each cross (not each pod) must be kept separate, and in the succeeding year or years, the progeny too of each cross should be carefully segregated and recorded.

The resultant plants from the cross-fertilised seed in the first generation are known technically as F^1s, or the F^1 generation. Usually the colour of the flowers of these F^1s is all the same, but different from either parent. Thus a cross between a dark-seeded white and a cream-pink might produce a crude red or even a purple or maroon in the F^1 stage. It is only when dealing with a cross in which one or both parents are untrue or unfixed that there is a variation in the colour of the F^1s. But in any case, no notice need be taken of the appearance of the flowers of this first generation. It is the next, or F^2 generation, in which the interesting variations occur. We now arrive at the first real stumbling block, namely the problem of what varieties to cross; and this is followed later by the even greater problem of knowing what variations to select and retain when the second or F^2 generation is in flower – the "grandchildren" of the original parents. Before examining these problems, it would be well to review in general unscientific terms what actually happens in crossing and, in brief, what basic laws of inheritance are involved.

Many will perhaps remember the pleasant surprise with which they learned at school, in their very first painting lessons, that certain colours when mixed produced different shades, maybe quite different colours. Mixing yellow and blue gave green, a small proportion of red with white produced pink, and so on. The hybridist does *not* mix and produce colours the same as a painter. For example, if one crosses any two dark-seeded creams together, or any two dark-seeded whites, most of their progeny will usually be coloured. Nor does the modern plant breeder rely on guesswork or make crosses indiscriminately in the hope that something useful may turn up. Exact results can rarely be foreseen; but the knowledge of what is likely to happen is sufficient to give more or less clear-cut aims and objectives, and this knowledge is enough to avoid years of experiment and expense. Only in comparatively recent times has this become possible.

Have we not all noticed that certain characteristics, peculiarities of habit, form and colour are hereditary? We take it for granted that these hereditary characteristics are handed down from generation to generation. Even with human beings we often remark that the colour of hair and eyes, disposition or intelligence have been inherited from certain parents or grandparents. We have come to recognise, perhaps unconsciously, that to a certain extent like produces like, and that pure fixed stocks breed true. For instance, we do not expect two dwarf green peas to produce talls, any more than we expect two pure bred fox terriers to produce a spaniel. The characteristics which distinguish variety from variety, breed from breed, in the plant and animal kingdoms vary little in succeeding generations. They are handed down intact. Nor can they, except by crossing, be altered by environment or other circumstances to any appreciable degree. For example, we have removed most of the tail from some breeds of sheep and dogs when they were young for many successive generations; but in the end we have not altered in the slightest the natural tendency of those breeds to produce long-tailed progeny. We can only bring about drastic changes in hereditary characteristics through hybridisation. There is very wide scope for activities in this field, but it also has its fairly obvious limits. Speaking generally, crosses can only be carried out among varieties of the same species, occasionally between varieties of the same genus but different species, and very rarely between varieties of a different genus. Of recent years, somewhat artificial methods have enabled hybrids to be produced which were not possible without them, but not to a sufficient degree to alter the general accuracy of this statement. In passing, it might be mentioned that both in the animal and vegetable kingdoms hybrids between different species are usually sterile.

As far as we can gather, the first man to become really curious about the behaviour of hereditary characteristics was Gregor Mendel, an Austro-Silesian priest born in 1822. His research in the field of hybridisation proved the starting point of a most fascinating branch of modern science. He found, by crossing varieties of plants and animals of the same species, but with widely different characteristics, that fixed laws governed the extent and ratio in which those characteristics were inherited. It will provide a good working knowledge if we follow one of his first experiments and his observations and records of what transpired in the first and subsequent generations of this particular cross. His method was to find two varieties of the same species, whose characteristics were opposite in one or more ways, and he found in culinary peas a subject which provided several of these pairs of opposite characteristics. For the purpose of this illustration we will take one pair of opposite characteristics only, namely tallness as opposed to dwarfness, and cross a tall culinary pea (as Mendel did) with a dwarf. We will assume that both parents are fixed, or true to name and character. In the first, or F^1, generation we might reasonably expect the plants to grow to a height halfway between their two very different parents, and would probably be very surprised when nothing of the kind actually happened. We should find, in fact, that all the offspring in the F^1 generation were tall like their tall parent. There would be no visible sign that one of their parents was a dwarf. Mendel found somewhat similar behaviour in other crosses, and the particular character which emerged almost intact in the F^1 generation he termed "dominant", for obvious reasons, whilst the character which was submerged or hidden in the first generation he called "recessive". Not by any means is it possible to find such a marked degree of dominance by one character over the other in every cross that is made; but in hybridising plants one finds that nearly all hereditary pairs of opposite characteristics can be classified as either dominant or recessive, although the extent of dominance may vary considerably.

Let us follow up this illustration of Mendel's culinary pea cross, a dwarf variety crossed with a tall. We saw that the first, or F^1, generation were all tall-growing plants like their tall parent, but what happens when we save seed from this F^1 generation? We shall find, as Mendel did, that the recessive factor, dwarfness, has re-asserted itself in one quarter of the total plants. If we carry these dwarf plants again to the third, fourth, or even fifth generation, we shall find that they remain perfectly true to dwarfness, and give no indication whatsoever, in succeeding generations, that one of their parents in the original cross was a tall. But what of the remaining 75 per cent tall plants in the F^2 generation? Though these were all tall, we find, if we save seed

Dynasty A vigorous variety with long, strong stems. Raised by Alan F. Robertson.

from them, that only one third will remain true to tallness in future generations, whilst the other two thirds (that is 50 per cent of the total F^2 generation) will again, in the F^3 generation, split up into the same proportion as did the F^2s, namely one quarter true dwarfs, one quarter true talls, and one half untrue or unfixed talls. The following illustration will make this somewhat involved explanation perfectly clear, and once these proportions are firmly fixed in one's mind, much of the difficulty of grasping an important basic principle of genetics will have been mastered.

A CULINARY PEA CROSS

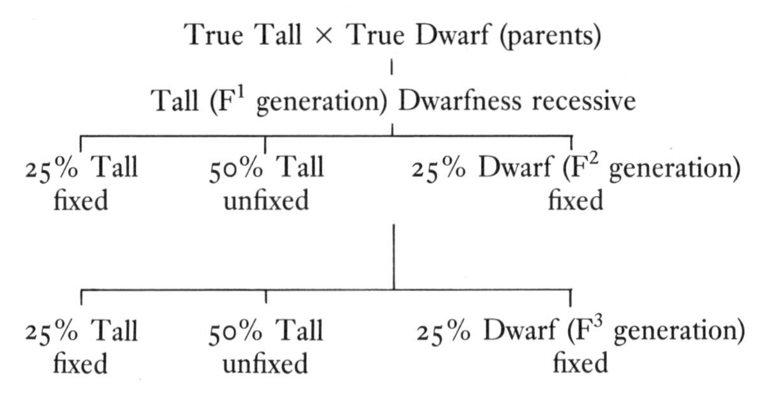

The illustration deals with one simple pair of quite opposite characteristics, which behave in a clearly recognisable manner when brought together by means of a cross. The whole thing becomes much more complicated when we endeavour to deal with more than one pair of opposite characteristics in the same cross. For example, if we cross a tall late culinary pea, having light green foliage, large pods, wrinkled seeds, and good culinary qualities, with a dwarf early pea with the opposite characteristics of dark green foliage, small pods, round seeds, and a poor flavour, we then have six pairs of opposing characteristics to contend with, which can theoretically combine with one another in a great many clear-cut and different ways. In actual practice, differences may not be clear-cut, and intermediate stages in height, size of pod, flavour or colour of foliage may multiply almost indefinitely the possible variations. In other words, it is usually necessary to raise a very large number of plants of the F^2 generation to be certain of bringing out in most crosses their full capacity of variations.

Generally speaking, the object of the plant hybridist is to combine in one individual plant two or more desirable characteristics which he finds in two separate varieties. As rough examples, one might select an early tomato, a heavy cropper, but very poor in quality and flavour, and cross this with another variety, possibly a late, the quality and flavour of the fruit of which were excellent. The breeder's object would of course be an early tomato which cropped well, and which produced good fruit of good quality and flavour. A small flat onion, with exceptional keeping qualities, might be crossed with a large globe onion which did not keep well, the objective being a good keeper which was large and globe shaped. Coming back to Sweet Peas – at almost any period of their history there have always been one or two varieties which excelled in size of bloom, and one of the obvious objectives of raisers has been to combine that size with other colours. These simple illustrations will serve to show the general direction or trend of the plant breeder's thoughts and efforts. Very few individual varieties of any one kind of plant can be called really perfect or ideal, and the hybridist is for ever striving to impart some variation, be it ever so slight, to effect improvement.

This brings us to another major difficulty of the hybridist. It is a simple matter to bring desirable characteristics possessed by two varieties together in one cross, but it is not by any means certain that these will combine in one plant. In the F^1 generation they are combined, and in a way reduced to a state of flux, but in the following F^2 generation they do not always behave in the manner one hopes, for whilst we find that some of them link up and combine, attracting each other as magnet attracts steel, others are like oil and water which, when brought together in the same receptacle, will still keep quite separate. One could quote instances of this attraction and repulsion, even in human beings. We usually associate dark hair with dark eyes, and very rarely find, say, dark eyes in conjunction with naturally fair hair. The plant hybridist would have a comparatively easy task if all the desirable qualities which are to be found within the scope of any one species could be obtained in conjunction with one another simply by crossing together those varieties which possess them.

There is almost an art in knowing what varieties to cross in order to produce worthwhile results. I would go even further and advance the belief that a few individuals are particularly gifted in this way – which directly leads to the surmise that hybridists are "born, not made". Be this as it may, I find it difficult to express or explain in general terms any clear-cut policy which may be followed by the Sweet Pea hybridist. Yet there are some indications which can be given, and which I trust may be found helpful. If a new Sweet Pea is introduced which shows decided improvement in colour or size, obviously this should be crossed with other varieties which lack its particular qualities. The disappointing feature is that others are just as likely to see such possibilities as oneself, and in any case the raisers of these particular varieties have had the advantage of working on them some years before they are made available to everyone. Here the beginner is at a decided disadvantage until, after a few years, he is able to confine his crosses, at least with one parent, to his own seedlings. For this reason, practically all the crosses I have made for many years have had one, often two, of my unnamed seedlings as parents, and I have avoided, as far as possible, crosses which other hybridists may have made, or are making. It is hardly necessary to say that only by using the best material available can one hope to make progress. It would be interesting to know the pedigrees of some of our favourite modern kinds; but these are rarely made public, for as in my own case, a proportion of the ancestors involved may be seedlings which have never been named or offered. It is advisable to use only large-flowered, vigorous parents, though the temptation to use two parents which are not very large may be great. Comparatively small-flowered and weaker growing kinds should only be crossed together with the object of providing a colour basis for future crosses.

The general tendency I believe is to confine crosses to varieties or seedlings which are unrelated, or as distantly related as possible, and to avoid inbreeding. Yet from years of practical experience, I am confident that judicious inbreeding often achieves quicker and more certain results than any other breeding method. Inbreeding can be applied as effectively to Sweet Peas as to other plants, birds and mammals. To clarify what is meant by inbreeding I will give a straightforward illustration. We will assume that a new Sweet Pea of unusual size has been introduced, and will call it *Red Giant*. We will further suppose *Red Giant* has been crossed with a much smaller-flowered, but beautifully coloured, salmon-cerise unnamed seedling. Quite good coloured salmon-cerises have appeared in the F^2 generation of this cross, but there is still a lack of size in them all. Such a state of affairs need not be discouraging, for the ultimate attainment of one's object is often only a matter of patience. The best of the salmon-cerise seedlings should be carried to the F^3 generation to find out if any are true or fixed, and if one is proved true it should be crossed back to its parent, *Red Giant*. If this cross does not produce the desired size of flower, combined with the salmon-cerise colour one requires, the same procedure should be followed, and the progeny (provided one at least was of the desired colour and true) should again be crossed back to *Red Giant*. It will be seen that *Red Giant* is therefore not only the parent, but the grandparent and great-grandparent as well, of the resulting plants. In point of fact they will carry seven-eighths *Red Giant* "blood". Unless the repulsion factor I have previously mentioned is very pronounced, the chances of ultimately obtaining the desired result, namely, a seedling with the size of *Red Giant* and the colour of the original salmon-cerise seedling, would be very "rosy".

One sometimes hears or reads the term "line-breeding" as distinct from inbreeding, though to my mind the two are the same, except that line-breeding usually implies a modified form of inbreeding, and can briefly, and perhaps rather loosely, be described as keeping within one family. In this sense we have always line-bred Sweet Peas, though the "families" and the direction have been subject to change. Where one finds that crosses with a particular variety give a large proportion of seedlings which are really good, this is a variety which lends itself to inbreeding. An instance that comes very readily to mind is *The Fawn.* I realised immediately when I saw this American introduction that it would probably open up a new range of colour tones, and within a few years we had a batch of new salmon, orange-salmon, salmon-scarlet, salmon-cerise, salmon-pink, and salmon cream-pink shades which were perfectly sunproof, but which all gave thin-skinned seed, liable to rot during germination. We found it very difficult to work up stocks of these new shades, and after one particularly poor harvest decided that it was useless trying to increase and introduce them. However, further crosses were carried out with the object of obtaining those same beautiful tones in seedlings which had not this annoying tendency for the seeds to rot. Results were not very exciting, but a few first-class seedlings were raised and have very probably made the whole thing worthwhile.

Inbreeding can be practised to introduce qualities other than size of bloom. Colour, vigour, the capacity for producing more than four blooms on a stem, form, the tendency to give duplex and triplex standards, all provide lines of development amenable to this process. Speaking in general terms, there is, in my opinion, no better or quicker method whereby desirable qualities can be introduced and fixed. But let there be no mistake: I do not advocate inbreeding or even line-breeding as a simple infallible policy to be blindly followed. It provides pitfalls and dangers far greater than are met with when crossing unrelated varieties. Whilst inbreeding may concentrate and fix desirable qualities, it is just as liable to do exactly the same thing with undesirable characteristics. It will almost certainly bring to light weaknesses or defects inherent in the make-up of the predominant "blood". It is therefore an obvious precaution to make certain, as far as is reasonably possible, that the varieties one uses are free from inherent defects. Should weakness or an undesirable character of any kind crop up with inbreeding, that is the time to come to a full stop with the strain or strains concerned. I hope it may not appear too contradictory or involved to state that an unwanted characteristic, or even a weakness, can usually be either eradicated or else submerged by inbreeding to a variety which is exactly the opposite in that particular respect.

Turning again from Sweet Peas to the field of plants in general, and to Gregor Mendel's discoveries in particular, one could give from personal experience many instances where his research has proved invaluable. But this is a Sweet Pea book, and one hesitates to introduce other subjects, interesting though they may be. However, hybridisation is so fascinating that I feel, having gone so far, that the reader might welcome a brief diversion. The two well-known types of dwarf Dahlias raised and introduced by my firm – *Unwins Dwarf Hybrids* and *Unwins Ideal Bedding* – came originally from crosses I made between the single dwarf scarlet *Coltness Gem* and varieties of the tall semi-double type known as *Charm* Dahlias. Remembering the hybridist's general aim to combine the desirable qualities found in two varieties or types in one individual, it was my direct intention to raise a dwarf semi-double race of Dahlias with a wide colour range. This proved simple. In the F^1 generation of this cross all the plants were tall and gave single flowers, which plainly showed me that the two qualities I really wanted were recessives. I thus knew that any semi-double dwarf plants found in the second or F^2 generation, if segregated, would breed true to these characteristics, and so it proved. Approximately one in sixteen of the F^2 generation were dwarf in habit, semi-double in form of flower, and these kept true to these characteristics in succeeding generations. The point I wish to make is that, after seeing what the F^1 generation was like, I could then go ahead, knowing full well my objective was well within reach. In the same way, some years ago, finding an Aquilegia with a very sweet scent, but with only rudimentary spurs, I crossed this with the long-spurred type in the hope of raising a long-spurred race of scented Aquilegias. Here again, luck was on my side, for the F^1 generation gave all non-scented, spurless flowers. The scented spurred flowers came along in the second generation, in almost exactly Mendelian proportions – about one plant in every sixteen – and they bred true to these characteristics.

Turning from flowers to vegetables, one has found in tomatoes that the potato-leaved type is true recessive, as is also yellow fruit colouring and the bush or dwarf habit of growth. To illustrate further the help which this knowledge of genetic laws gives to the hybridist, I will – on paper – make a particular tomato cross which I am certain has never been made previously, either by me or by anyone else. Yet in this cross I can quite easily, and with reasonable accuracy, forecast what will happen. We will suppose that my aim is to raise a new yellow tomato, with potato-leaved foliage, and with the extremely dwarf and distinctive habit of *The Amateur* (a variety we introduced in 1951). *The Amateur* is red-fruited and has the ordinary kind of leaves. Among our F^2 tomato crosses I notice a true or fixed seedling of usual height but with "potato-type" foliage and bright yellow fruit. We will therefore theoretically make our cross between this latter and *The Amateur*, for all three characteristics we want are found in these two. Let us set these characteristics down on paper and see what our problem looks like:

The Amateur	*Yellow Seedling*
Red Fruit (Dominant)	Yellow Fruit (Recessive)
Ordinary Leaves (Dominant)	Potato-leaves (Recessive)
Bush Habit (Recessive)	Tall Habit (Dominant)

I have underlined the qualities we are aiming to combine in one plant. Two of them are found in one parent, one in the other. We commence with the great advantage of knowing in advance which are dominant and which recessive. We know therefore that all plants from this cross in the first or F^1 generation will be tall growing, bear red fruit, and have ordinary foliage – just ordinary looking tomatoes. But what happens if we save seed from these and grow it on? I invite the reader at this point to close this book and work out on paper the ratio in which the three opposite pairs of characteristics will be transmitted to the progeny of this cross in the second or F^2 generation, and later to compare results with mine.

For our own convenience only we will assume that sixty-four plants have been raised in this F^2 generation. In such a cross as this we should, in actual practice, raise four or five times this number to be certain of getting at least one plant with the qualities we are aiming at. However, we have, as I have said, intentionally assumed for our own convenience that we have only sixty-four plants to deal with in the F^2 stage. We will now further assume that the ratio of the characteristics involved will behave in exactly correct genetic manner, even though we know full well that a very much greater number of plants must be raised before we dare expect such accurate results. The red colour of fruit is dominant, so we may expect 75 per cent of the plants (forty-eight plants) to bear red fruit, 25 per cent (sixteen plants) to bear yellow fruit. But there are two other characteristics to bear in mind: habit of growth and type of foliage. Take the red-fruited plants first. 75 per cent of these (thirty-six plants) will be of dominant tall-growing habit, 25 per cent (twelve plants) will be dwarfs. In the thirty-six tall red-fruit plants, twenty-seven will have ordinary foliage (also dominant), nine will possess potato-type leaves. In like manner, nine of the twelve dwarf red-fruited plants will have ordinary foliage, three plants will have potato-like leaves. Of the sixteen yellow-fruited plants, 75 per cent (twelve plants) will be talls, 25 per cent (four plants) dwarfs. Nine of the yellow talls will have ordinary foliage, three the potato-like leaves. In the four yellow-fruited dwarf plants three will have ordinary foliage, and only one the potato-like leaves.

These are the exact Mendelian proportions we may theoretically expect; and in actual practice when dealing with large numbers, it is remarkable how near the expected ratio are the usual results. The ordinary factor of chance operates, and like tossing a coin, though "heads" may come up more times than "tails" over a short number of tosses, we know that over a large number things will even up and the certainty of a 50–50 chance will be upheld. We could take this particular illustration of a tomato cross a stage further, and accurately forecast what would happen to the eight clear-cut variations in the F^2 generation if we saved their seed separately and took them to the F^3 and subsequent generations. However, we started out with the object of raising a dwarf-growing, yellow-fruited, potato-leaved new variety, and have found that it takes, on an average, sixty-four seedlings in the F^2 generation to produce one of these. Having obtained it we do know that it will breed true to all three of the characteristics we aimed at, for all three – yellow colour, dwarf habit and potato-like foliage – are recessive, and as Mendel found out, recessive characters always breed true. Thus the reader will appreciate that even a slight knowledge of the laws governing inheritance gives the hybridist the opportunity of working with a good deal more confidence than by the haphazard methods which would otherwise be unavoidable. The accompanying diagram will, I hope, give rather a clearer picture of what happens in this particular tomato cross than my written explanation.

DIAGRAMATIC RECONSTRUCTION OF THE TOMATO CROSS

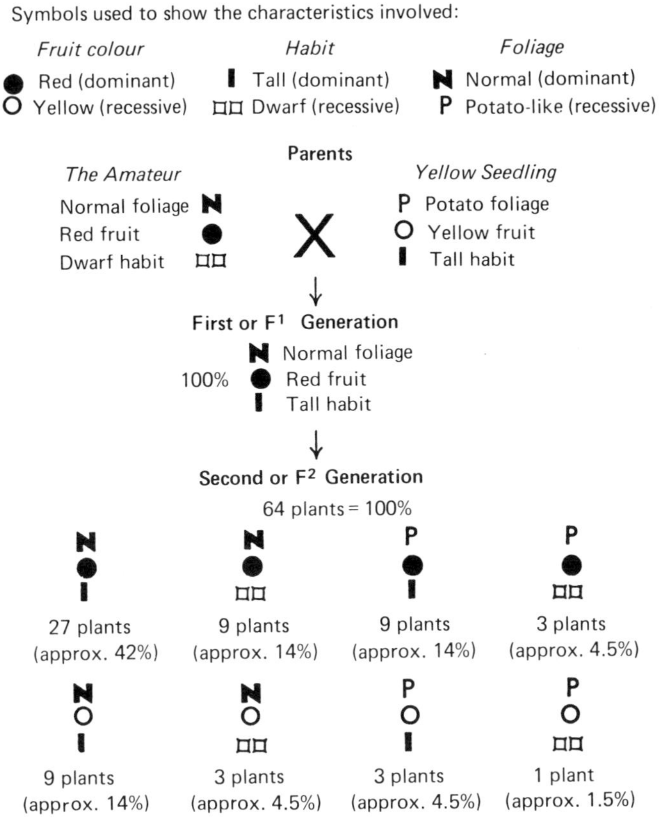

Symbols used to show the characteristics involved:

Fruit colour	*Habit*	*Foliage*
● Red (dominant)	▮ Tall (dominant)	N Normal (dominant)
O Yellow (recessive)	◻◻ Dwarf (recessive)	P Potato-like (recessive)

Parents

The Amateur
Normal foliage N
Red fruit ●
Dwarf habit ◻◻

X

Yellow Seedling
P Potato foliage
O Yellow fruit
▮ Tall habit

↓

First or F¹ Generation

100%
N Normal foliage
● Red fruit
▮ Tall habit

↓

Second or F² Generation

64 plants = 100%

N ● ▮	N ● ◻◻	P ● ▮	P ● ◻◻
27 plants (approx. 42%)	9 plants (approx. 14%)	9 plants (approx. 14%)	3 plants (approx. 4.5%)
N O ▮	N O ◻◻	P O ▮	P O ◻◻
9 plants (approx. 14%)	3 plants (approx. 4.5%)	3 plants (approx. 4.5%)	1 plant (approx. 1.5%)

An even more easily understood illustration of the Mendelian law than the tomato cross can be given this time from actual experience. Nearly fifty years ago I became interested in what was then a new type of Dahlia called *Paeony Flowered*. There were, at that time, no dwarf Dahlias. Then Dobbies of Edinburgh found a dwarf of eighteen inches with single scarlet blooms and named it *Coltness Gem*. Examples of it were exhibited at Chelsea Show by John Forbes of

Hawick, and when I saw them I was struck with the certainty that a cross between *Coltness Gem* and *Paeony Flowered* would produce a dwarf semi-double type which would breed true from seed. I made the cross and the next year all plants of the F[1] generation were tall-growing with single flowers – just what I wanted and expected. They were in almost exact Mendelian proportions: 75% talls, 25% dwarfs. The tall plants were easily recognised in the small seedling stage and were not planted out. The dwarfs also came in Mendelian proportions, 25% of them having semi-double flowers in a wide and very attractive range of colours. I saved the tubers of these and planted them in a big bed far enough away from any other Dahlias to be certain that cross fertilisation could not take place through wind or insects. As I expected, seed from this bed came perfectly true to type and I called them *Unwins Dwarf Hybrids*. To cut a long story short they were immediately popular and still are. I am proud that they are grown extensively in every country in the world where Dahlias will grow.

Perhaps it should be explained here that after a cross has been made, the flowers in the F[1] and F[2] generations are not again artificially cross-fertilised, but allowed to self-fertilise in the natural manner. Invariably, little notice need be taken of an F[1] generation, except for the indication it gives as to which characters are dominant and which recessive. In some crosses it is impossible to be very sure in this direction, for though in many cases the F[1]s closely resemble one parent, there are many crosses where they will either be somewhere between the two parents, or, as with most Sweet Pea crosses, unlike either of them.

Now we turn our attention back to Sweet Peas. As we have seen, one has to await the F[2] generation before results can be estimated, and this is naturally the most exciting time of all for the enthusiastic hybridist. He will find that the different Sweet Pea crosses split up into all shades, giving a complete kaleidoscope of colour. It is fascinating at flowering time to watch the blooms open every day, and the reader will imagine the eagerness with which the rows of crosses are searched for any seedlings which may show signs of improvement or any which may be distinct. It is in this work of selecting the most promising seedlings that experience and good judgment count heavily. There is little point in spending time on crossing and then failing to recognise improvements (if there be any) when the crosses mature. But better that than the really bad judgment which leads to selecting worthless seedlings in the first instance, and later, after a good deal of work and time have been expended on them, discovering they are poor. The Sweet Pea hybridist will find out sooner or later that it is very unwise to pass a hasty judgment on a seedling. First impressions are not usually conclusive. The rows must be watched every day or two for weeks, and the plants which have been marked for future observation closely examined, to find out how they react under varying weather conditions, and indeed in different light. Flowers of the best standard named varieties should be available for comparison, for there are very few experts capable of carrying colour and form in the mind's eye with any great degree of accuracy. Needless to say, plants which have stood the test of constant inspection and which still appear to be improvements should be carefully labelled and numbered and their seeds saved separately.

Any reader who may feel inclined to experiment in crossing Sweet Peas should grow the plants naturally, without restriction, under ordinary field culture. Nor should the ground be too well manured, or the setting of the seed may be prejudiced by too sappy a growth. Further, I think it is easier to recognise real improvements when the plants have not been particularly well grown. It is very difficult to assess the actual value of a new seedling at this stage. A careful examination of a single flower against other flowers of similar colouring will not reveal differences so obviously as comparing a bunch of each.

Though I have crossed and selected Sweet Peas since school-days, and through experience have, I believe, a fair idea as to which seedlings are likely to be worth saving, yet I always greatly value the candid opinions and carefully note the reactions of inexperienced friends who happen to be inspecting my crosses and selections. It is, of course, the ordinary grower rather than the enthusiast who really determines ultimate public opinion. A factor which sometimes proves deceptive lies in the tendency of some Sweet Peas to change their colour tones slightly as autumn approaches. The degree of variation admittedly is very minor; but there is a certain deepening or enriching of the colours as the flowering season goes by, more particularly in autumn-sown plants. One is always tempted to overdo things and to save too many selections, and with me this temptation has never lessened. Unless this natural tendency is stoutly resisted, within a few years (if crossing and selection continue) the number of selections on hand in the "workshop" stage will prove somewhat confusing and embarrassing.

We broke off from our observation of the Sweet Pea crosses at the point where we labelled the seedlings of our choice in the F^2 stage and saved their seeds separately; but before proceeding to the next

Wire-edged seedling on trial at Wisley.
Courtesy of J.R.F. Bishop

generation I will mention one other point that I think quite important. If a particular cross has produced a large proportion of really good seedlings, it is wise to save seed *in mixture* from the plants which have not been labelled, for quite probably in the next generation, possibly in the next two or three generations, this cross will split up again, releasing new shades, new variations each year. It all depends on the parents; but the number of distinct colours which one single cross will sometimes produce is truly amazing. Unless one has been unduly fortunate, probably by the end of the season it will be found that no more than one per cent of the F^2s have been labelled for future use.

The single plant selections from the F^2s are duly sown and kept separate, and when they flower the beginner will experience his first really acute disappointment, for again, unless undue luck is on one's side, it will be found that only a small minority of the seedlings will

Can-Can Raised by Charles Unwin.

come true to type and colour. The remainder will split up again, not often to the same extent as the F^2s, but the variation will be wide in some instances. It is not wise to discard these unfixed stocks offhand as of no further use. Where the percentage of "rogues" or wrong colours is small, and the seedling is sufficiently worthy, it is a good plan to pull up the wrong plants and save the seed of say, a half dozen or more of the remainder separately, in the hope that one or more of these single plant cultures will prove fixed the following year. Looking back, I was somewhat surprised to discover what a large percentage of the new Sweet Peas we have introduced have been raised from stocks which in the first instance were unfixed. Again, every one of the unfixed stocks should be daily inspected as if they were F^1s, for there will probably be quite a number of variations worthy of saving singly and growing on.

It may be several years before a sufficient quantity of seed is available of any one selection for public distribution. The work of the hybridist is, therefore, at first sight a lengthy business. If one makes a cross, say in 1986, it is unlikely that the possible results of that cross will be ready in marketable quantity before 1992 or 1993. The great specialist firms who raise Sweet Peas on a fairly extensive scale rarely offer more than one or two new varieties each season, and the reader may wonder why so few seedlings ultimately find their way into the catalogues. I do not know what may be the experience of others in this respect; but in my own case, quite a number of good fixed new varieties have been consigned to the mixed bag simply because another raiser has marketed a very similar or identical new one just before mine was ready. This causes a good deal of disappointment, of course. But taking the broad view, it is of little consequence who introduces a really good new Sweet Pea. The great point is that it has been raised and made available to the public.

I fear I may have painted too black a picture of the trials and difficulties, the lengthy wait for ultimate results, and the inevitable discouragements of the hybridist. If this should be so, I do assure my readers that the very great pleasure and absorbing interest one derives from the work much more than repays for its set-backs. It is surprising that more amateur growers have not taken up hybridisation, for quite apart from the financial side of the question, the enjoyment which varieties of one's own raising gives to others is particularly gratifying. It is quietly satisfying to realise that one may be a link – maybe only a tiny link – in that great chain of raisers whose aim has been the improvement of the Sweet Pea, both before and since the time of Henry Eckford.

To the raiser, the financial side of things cannot be entirely disregarded, and if he wishes to make his work a financial success, public taste must be studied, sometimes against his own inclinations. Hundreds of times have I reluctantly passed over in the F^2 stage seedlings which I have considered very beautiful and quite distinct, knowing only too well what would be the verdict of the general public. In course of time I have come to realise that I admire the soft "pastel" tones to rather a greater extent than is general. Bright, decided, clear-cut colours are the "sellers". Anything which, though beautiful and distinct, may remotely deserve the descriptions "washy", "insipid", "undecided", "neither one thing nor the other", "curious", "freakish", is best avoided unless one can afford the somewhat risky policy of attempting to "educate" the public. Seedlings which fade in the sun or lose their brightness in water should also be discarded, whatever other qualities they may possess.

We can safely accept the dictum that public taste is right, for the history of the flower does not, to my knowledge, furnish one single instance of a poor variety ever becoming very popular. In reverse, there have been few really first-class varieties which have ultimately failed to become recognised as such.

Many years ago, my father raised a complete series of striped and veined Spencers from crosses with that unique old Grandiflora *Helen Pierce*, on both cream and white ground colours. The colour of the markings differed considerably on the various seedlings. Three of the worst were eventually named and introduced. The best, most of them very lovely peas indeed, were such "shy" seeders that it was a practical impossibility to work up enough stock to offer. We persevered for some years, but a bad season for seeding finished them off, and I believe my father was relieved rather than annoyed, for they had provided us with a long spell of tedious frustration. At the time of writing we are back at a similar stage with some larger-flowered stripes, and it appears probable that the behaviour of these may compensate for the previous fiasco. But these new stripes seed normally, and some of the best are proving rather stubborn to fix.

This difficulty of fixing seems much more pronounced in the seedlings of some crosses than others, and I well remember one of the first crosses I ever made in this connection. It was between *Clara Curtis* and *Eric Harvey*. Practically nothing worth saving cropped up in the F^2s apart from a large cream, flushed mauve. This was saved, and the next season it split up into a whole series of flushes, no two seedlings being exactly alike. They ranged from violet-blue to light lavender, and from deep cherry pink to flesh, both on cream and white grounds. Only two of these ever reached the public, and these two were by no means the most attractive members of a most remarkable family. We found the remainder quite unstable and impossible to fix.

One could go on reminiscing like this; but I feel I have written enough to give my reader a good idea of the methods adopted by the plant breeder, and also of the wholly fascinating mixture of intense interest, pleasure, and disappointment which the work of hybridisation involves. Plant breeding grows on one, and though the beginner almost invariably starts with one subject, sooner or later, should circumstances permit, there is the inevitable urge to extend one's activities to other subjects. Almost instinctively one begins to estimate the possibilities and probabilities of working with other flowers or vegetables which may attract one's personal interest. Apart from hybridising many different kinds of flowers and some vegetables, I have derived a good deal of interest and pleasure through hybridising such varied subjects as domestic fowls, rabbits, and budgerigars, and have achieved most of my objectives with each of these. It is a far cry from Sweet Peas to rabbits, or from rabbits to human beings; yet I have no doubt that the same hereditary laws apply to all. In passing, perhaps I might venture the assertion that practical experience in hybridisation has, with me, tended to give emphasis to the importance

Charles Unwin Raised by Rev. T.K. Colledge.

of the hereditary factor of circumstance and environment, in shaping the finished article, whether this be a plant, an animal, or a man. The old proverb dealing with the impossibility of making a silk purse out of a sow's ear is much more fully appreciated, but I must resist the temptation to carry this theme further.

I wholeheartedly commend this work of hybridisation to all who have the necessary time and inclination. Scientific cross-fertilisation is still practised by comparatively very few, in spite of the fact that greater opportunities in this direction were never more apparent. Often the length of time one has to wait for results is advanced as a serious deterrent; but, after all, crosses "mature" in three generations, and in period of actual time this only means two years with annuals such as Sweet Peas. It takes just as long for a rose bed or an herbaceous border to reach perfection, longer still for a fruit tree to come into real bearing. The first period of waiting is the last, for if crosses are made every year, then each season after the first batch reach the F^2 stage, other F^2s are coming along annually to maintain and increase one's interest. But two maxims should never be forgotten by the beginner: firstly, do not waste time on mediocre seedlings; secondly, make quite certain that garden space, energy, or your time, are not overtaxed by more plants, more crosses and selections than can be comfortably and efficiently handled.

It might be considered that with the Sweet Pea there are at present as many hybridists taking an active part in its development as its capacity will permit. Chances may not appear too good of starting

Colin Unwin Raised by Rev. T.K. Colledge.

Unwins Mixed Stripes

from scratch and succeeding against raisers who have the undoubted advantages of experience and exclusive advanced new "material" to work with. The beginner may, perhaps rightly, consider that there are many other flowers, vegetables, or even fruits, birds, or animals, which offer richer prospects and greater opportunities than the Sweet Pea. But whatever field is selected, I most earnestly advise the enthusiast to go ahead with the most encouraging example of Henry Eckford as a reminder of what great influence one man can exert on his chosen subject. In lesser degree, the example of Bernard R. Jones and the Rev. T. K. Colledge with Sweet Peas proves what can be done by spare-time amateur raisers.

CHAPTER X

SEED GROWING

Though few amateur growers will wish to save their own seed there are a good many points of general interest connected with the business of growing Sweet Peas for seed which I propose to deal with in this chapter. About seventy years ago an average retail price for twelve varieties packeted separately, one hundred seeds of each, was 2s. 6d. A total of 1,200 seeds, roughly a ¼ lb. in weight, for half-a-crown, seems fantastically cheap these days. However, fifty years ago a good collection of twelve varieties, twenty-five seeds of each, cost around 3s. to 3s. 6d. – over four times as much. But at the time of writing a similar collection of ten varieties, twenty-five seeds of each, costs between £3 and £4 – the price having increased twenty to thirty-fold on the first figures quoted. What is the reason for these three extraordinary differences in price in the three periods? The fact that everything has risen in cost only partly furnishes the explanation. In the first instance, seventy years ago, we were dealing with Grandiflora varieties, which, in California, seeded four to five times heavier than the early Spencers. In this country the difference was even more marked, particularly in a wet, cool summer. Modern varieties, generally speaking, do not seed as well as the early Spencers – not altogether surprisingly for it is almost an invariable rule that the more highly any species is developed, the greater becomes the difficulty of perpetuating it. But apart from this we find quite a logical explanation of the variation in cropping capacity between Spencers and Grandifloras in the differences in structure of the flowers themselves. The keel of a flower of Grandiflora type is smaller that that of a Spencer and fits tightly round the stamens and stigma, clamping them closely together, whilst its upper edges meet. It will be appreciated that when the pollen is ripe, and the stamens burst, the stigma is completely surrounded by ripe pollen, held there by the gentle pressure of the keel. Neither wind nor rain cause any disturbance, and in consquence almost every flower eventually produces a well-filled seed pod. In the case of the Spencers, a comparison will immediately show a vital difference of formation. The Spencer keel is larger, less curved, much more baggy, and the top edges, instead of touching, are more or less widely separated. To distinguish between the two we use the terms "clamped keel" in the case of the Grandifloras and "open keel" for the Spencers, both for obvious reasons. In the open keel, stamens and stigma are held together and the quantity of pollen transferred from anthers to stigma is thus greatly diminished. Further, there is a tendency for the stigma to develop comparatively more quickly than the petals in the case of the Spencers, sometimes to the extent of the top of the stigma slightly protruding from the front or bow of the keel in the bud stage. Thus the chance of a Spencer flower being fertilised is very much less than that of a Grandiflora, this difference being decidedly more marked in wet, cold weather.

Most of the Sweet Pea seed sold in this country is now grown in California, whose sub-tropical climate is very much more suitable for Sweet Pea seed production than our own uncertain summer and autumn. The weather conditions there are nearer those of Malta, the home of the Sweet Pea, with the rainy seasons and periods of drought falling in both countries at about the same times each year. In the valleys of California the soil has plenty of depth and conserves moisture to a remarkable degree during the long hot and dry summer. The plants make wonderful growth, and although it is usual to sow in rows three or four feet apart, and not support the plants in any way, they attain a height of four or five feet, the length of haulm being much greater. Yet, in spite of this great vigour, growth is "hard", not sappy, through the glorious sunshine. On the various seed-growing farms, or ranches, it is customary to grow large areas of one variety, separating these from other varieties by belts of other kinds of flowers and vegetables also being grown for seed. This method not only reduces the chances of accidental mixing or cross-fertilisation, but makes harvesting easier and safer. Irrigation is usually necessary and the only real drawback is attacks of aphids in some seasons. The pods are not hand-picked, but the crop is cut like a corn crop here when it is judged that the bulk of the pods are ripe. After a short period of drying the seed is threshed out by machinery, cleaned, and the dust, small seeds, and any foreign matter removed. The result is usually a good sample.

In California, rogueing – the term we use for the operation of pulling out wrong colours or types in order to ensure trueness – is not an easy task with such a vast quantity of plants grown without supports. How it is done at present I do not know, but before the

Sweet Pea Snoopea growing for seed in California *courtesy of Denholm Seeds*

Second World War the work was carried out under expert supervision by Chinese and Japanese labourers who, within their limits, were very efficient. I have had the opportunity many times of comparing results from Sweet Peas of the same variety coming from various sources – California, British Columbia, the Continent, New Zealand, Australia, and our own English. In an average year there was little to choose between good English and New Zealand samples. The Californian samples were usually slightly smaller, though bright and clean in appearance. From other sources the seed varied too much to permit a general comparison. In a poor season here, most foreign and colonial Sweet Peas gave a better germination than our own, the Californian and New Zealand varieties usually slightly ahead of all others. As trueness to name depended so much on the care the skill of the individual grower, conclusive comparisons are hardly possible in this respect. I wish I could say that our home-grown seed was always more true than from other sources, but there have been many occasions when it has proved very disappointing. After repeated trials I must confess that I have found three or four seed houses in America which consistently produced Sweet Peas as true to name and colour as the English seed growers. This fact, together with the reliance which could always be placed on the germination of the Californian, made the latter an attractive proposition, particularly as they could be produced at about one-third the price of home-grown seed, or even less. Further, several of the American seed houses are quite willing to grow on contract from English-grown stock seed.

Champagne Bubbles Raised by Charles Unwin.

There is yet another factor in favour of Californian and New Zealand Sweet Pea seed from the point of view of the English seedsman. Provided well-harvested Sweet Pea seed is properly stored it will retain its vitality or germinating power for several years. The varieties vary slightly in longevity, but I have stored Sweet Pea seed for up to seven years, and, as far as could be judged, results from this old seed were fully equal to those from the current year's harvest. Actually I would much prefer to use old foreign-grown seed which had been tested, both for trueness and germination, rather than new English-grown seed harvested in a poor season.

A very large proportion of the Sweet Pea seed grown in this country comes from Essex. Probably the very best conditions are found within a comparatively small area near Coggeshall, where the rainfall is light, and the soil conducive to "hard" growth. In warm, dry years, reasonably good crops may be expected from almost any district south of the Wash from plants sown in the autumn. Ideal seed producing soil should be well drained, a little on the light side, not too rich, and if it contains a fair proportion of small stones, so much the better. Sappy, unripened growth is avoided by giving as long a growing or ripening period as our seasons permit. Heavy manuring is quite unnecessary –

indeed, in most years this course would be decidedly harmful, for the plants would produce too much growth at the expense of seed. Not only is the seed sown early in the autumn, either directly in the open, or, more frequently, in pots in a cold frame, but planting out from the pots is carried out as early in the spring as weather and soil conditions permit. It will be gathered that an early preparation of the soil is very important.

I do not like a rich soil for seed production. Plenty of space between rows is necessary and these should be five to six feet apart, running from north to south, thus ensuring a maximum of air and light. The plants begin to bloom at the end of May or early June, and if no flowers are removed, seed pods soon appear. These act somewhat like a brake on the growth of the plants, which become short-jointed, hard and woody. The first pods ripen in August when hand-picking commences, the pods being laid out to dry, or bagged and hung up in an airy outhouse or greenhouse. Care must be taken to prevent the pods that are not quite ripe becoming mildewed, and it is also essential that the different varieties are correctly labelled and kept quite separate at all stages. If open trays are used for the final ripening, precautions must be taken against odd seeds suddenly popping open, for when they burst they sometimes throw a seed or two for many yards. When the pods are dry and the seed hard, they are threshed out and dressed, the pods, dust and small seeds being removed by sieves and winnowing machines. At a later stage, all weather-stained, mouldy, flat, or badly split seeds are removed by hand to ensure a clean, bright sample and a high germination percentage. Just prior to packeting, most seed firms take the precaution of testing all stocks for germination and, this proving satisfactory, the seed is machine-packeted.

Briefly, that is the outline of Sweet Pea seed-growing in England. Many details not likely to interest the amateur have been omitted. The seed grower, of course, encounters the usual cultural difficulties, but probably his worst handicap is the English climate. In mentioning the Californian methods I used the term "rogueing". As previously explained, a rogue implies any plant which does not conform exactly to the type or colour of the variety in which it is growing, and to "rogue" a crop is to pull up and destroy all such plants in order to prevent their seeds being harvested. Thus, a red Sweet Pea growing in a pink variety is a colour rogue, whilst a pink Grandiflora cropping up in the stock of a Spencer variety of the same colour is a type rogue. Some rogues are the result of accidental mixing, but this is rare.

Usually they are due to the stock being inherently unfixed – that is to say, the stock produces a proportion of rogues each year, no matter what steps are taken to remove rogues the previous year. Very rarely have I seen a row of any length of one variety in which no rogues whatever have appeared. Thus 100 per cent trueness cannot reasonably be expected, even though the percentage of rogues with most modern varieties is small enough to be termed insignificant. On occasion, the presence of an unduly large number of rogues in a stock may be due to deterioration. I have experienced many instances where seedlings, and even named varieties, have unexpectedly "gone to pieces" in this way. To the best of my belief the cause of sudden deterioration is unknown. If the value of the seedling or named variety makes the procedure worthwhile, the best method is to save the seed separately from each of a number of plants of correct colour, in the hope that one or more of them will prove true.

Careful rogueing is vitally necessary to ensure a maximum degree of trueness of stocks, but it is a job for the expert. The great majority of rogues are worthless, yet each one should be carefully examined before it is pulled up, for many excellent varieties have originated as rogues or mutations. Had they not been "spotted" and their value recognised in time, they would, of course, have been lost. After all it is a simple matter to tie a label on any rogue that appears promising and to save the seed separately. Incidentally, from experience I would say that the chance of a rogue coming true is very much greater than that of an F^2 selection from a cross, provided the rogue is a real mutation and not the result of a mixture.

With the early Spencer varieties, type rogues sometimes proved a great nuisance. Being exactly the same colour as the correct flower it was not always easy to distinguish them, particularly in the case of varieties which normally produced a proportion of halfway-type rogues, flowers with a Grandiflora clamped keel but possessing a standard almost as large and wavy as the true Spencers. If seed was saved separately from these semi-Grandifloras, they usually reverted and produced a large proportion of true Grandifloras. As their seed-bearing capacity is equal to the old Grandifloras it will readily be seen that if they were not removed from a stock, within two or three years that stock would contain more Grandiflora-type rogues than true Spencer plants.

Another kind of rogue, which has now almost entirely disappeared, was exactly similar in colour and size to the variety in which it appeared, but the standards were "notched" – a legacy which came down from a rather poor type of Grandiflora. In these particular rogues the smooth rounded outline of the standard was broken towards the base by a cut, or notch, on each side. It is fortunate that this defect is rarely met with nowadays.

The presence of rogues can sometimes be detected in the seedling stage. Almost every reader will have noticed that most varieties have a coloured "wire edge", sometimes a flushing on their leaves, though in a few cases, notably white-seeded varieties and creams, there is no suspicion of colouring. This wire edge varies from palest brown to deep reddish brown, according to the variety, and experienced growers may even recognise quite a number of varieties at the seedling stage simply by this leaf colouring. At the flowering stage the colour in the axils of the leaves (that is the junction of the leaf stalk with the main stem) sometimes provides conclusive evidence in the case of a doubtful rogue.

Seeds differ in shape and colour very considerably in individual varieties, so even at the seed stage it is sometimes possible to discern rogues. For example, I found a white-seeded white variety, later named *Snowdon*, in a stock of the dark-seeded white variety *Gigantic*. Noticing a number of white seeds present in this stock of *Gigantic*, and dismissing the chance of an accidental mixture as extremely unlikely, I came to the conclusion that these were probably pure white mutations. I was reasonably sure that this particular stock of *Gigantic* had been properly rogued; further, I felt fairly confident that the flowers produced from the white seeds would not only be identical in character to *Gigantic*, but that they would be white, rather than of cream colouring. At that time *Gigantic* gave quite a large proportion of flowers very slightly tinted pink. As this defect would be impossible with a white-seeded white, the probable value of this mutation was obvious, so I straightaway sent most of the seeds to the N.S.P.S. Trials, keeping the remainder for stock. This rather saucy gamble "came off". My conclusions proved correct and the new white obtained an Award of Merit. I should think this is the one and only instance of a seedling obtaining an Award of Merit which neither the sender nor anyone else had previously seen in flower. At the time it embarrassed me considerably, for my perfectly accurate explanation of the origin of *Snowdon* was almost invariably received with ill-concealed scepticism.

It is unlikely that many rogues owe their origin to natural cross-fertilisation, for as already explained, the Sweet Pea is naturally self-pollinated, fertilisation taking place before the flower is fully open.

The Doctor A vigorous variety, well regarded for exhibition.

Bees and other insects, those very energetic and effective agents of cross-fertilisation in the case of a great many flowers, cannot, through the shape of the Sweet Pea keel and its other petals, gain access, at least not early enough. If this was not so, the marketing of true or fixed stocks of Sweet Peas would be very much more difficult. Wind, too, rarely carries Sweet Pea pollen, for not only is this protected by an enclosed keel, but the stigma is guarded in the same way. Yet, in spite of all this, I am quite certain that some rogues, particularly from stocks grown abroad, are neither mutations nor the result of mixing, nor are they what might be termed "natural rogues", arising from an unfixed stock. Some years ago, to satisfy my curiosity, I saved the seed of quite a number of rogues, separately, which appeared in stocks grown in California. They had intrigued me in the first place because they closely resembled F^1 crosses which I had made with the varieties concerned. In the F^2 generation they "split up" in exactly the same way as one expects crosses to behave; indeed, some were good enough to select and save. Unfortunately, my old records have been destroyed or it would have been possible to give a list of the varieties from which these selections came, also a list of the few which eventually were named and introduced. It is impossible to determine whether wind or insects were responsible for these natural crosses, but probably it was the former, with the odd pollen grain blowing about and occasionally finding a home on the extreme sticky tip of a slightly protruding stigma. The very remote chance of this sort of thing happening in this country would be greatly increased under drier, warmer conditions. The chance of natural cross-fertilisation, slight and improbable though it may be, may nevertheless provide the reason why Californian growers separate variety from variety with other crops.

In our uncertain climate, at least one firm has adopted the practice of growing their choice kinds under glass, where it is possible to obtain a reasonably heavy crop of seed no matter what outdoor conditions may be like. One has reduced this greenhouse method to a fine art, growing the plants on cordons at first, cutting the early flowers for sale or exhibition, afterwards ceasing to remove side shoots, "layering", and then letting them grow in a natural, unrestricted manner. Provided they have been kept healthy, a worthwhile seed crop may be expected and the plants are thus made to do double service. As cordons, such plants may have been lowered once or twice, and it is only on their final journey up their supports that they are allowed to grow in a free, natural manner, and produce their seed. Incidentally, the quality of greenhouse-produced seed is usually excellent.

More than once I have been asked whether seed saved from cordon-grown plants will produce better results than field-grown seed of the same variety. Theoretically there should be no difference, even though the plants were the progeny of many successive generations of cordon-grown plants; but in practice I would prefer seed which was field-grown, though I am afraid I cannot advance any specific reason to explain this preference.

Perhaps I have dealt at too great length with the topic of seed growing and I certainly have no wish to exaggerate its difficulties. The amateur grower, purchasing his Sweet Pea seeds, rightly expects the seed to be of good quality, true to name and colour, and to be of good germination. But, if on occasion there should be a few plants of wrong colouring, I hope what I have said in this chapter may explain that if one or two plants in a hundred turn out to be rogues it does not necessarily imply that the seed grower has been negligent or incompetent. These rogues are often quite beyond the control of the most careful seedsman.

There are a number of hard-seeded varieties which are inclined to germinate irregularly through the seed coat being highly impervious to moisture. Such seed will lie for a very long time in the soil before germinating, and in the past I have carried out extensive experiments to find out whether this problem could be solved before the seeds are actually packeted. I used acids of various strengths, soaking the seeds for different periods, and although a process was evolved which would considerably help matters, I found that samples of the same variety grown in different places varied to such an extent in the manner in which they responded, that in the end I had to give up the idea as impracticable. The better the harvesting conditions, the harder and more impervious was the seed coat; so, of course, Californian-grown seeds usually gave more trouble in this direction than did the same varieties grown here. Many years ago, before the Californian growers perfected their methods of cleaning and grading the seeds, samples sometimes arrived which were dull and dusty in appearance, and in one season, when we had to rely largely on Californian seed through a bad harvest here, my father hit on the ingenious notion of brightening the samples by working the seed about in large sacks which had their inner surface lightly coated with lard. The very thin film of lard which covered the seeds certainly brightened them, and greatly improved the look of the sample, but later on, reports from customers of mice taking the seeds immediately they were sown reached such large and serious proportions that he never used the lard treatment again.

CHAPTER XI

LOOKING AHEAD

Everyone connected with Sweet Peas – the ordinary amateur grower, the exhibitor, the raiser, and the seedsman – must of necessity be interested in the future of the flower. We all sometimes wonder what changes (if any) will take place in Sweet Peas during the next decade or so. We know that in all branches of horticulture there is continual restless effort on the part of hybridists to produce something new and distinct, to effect some improvement on existing varieties. The reason is easily seen, for it is simply another case of supply and demand. The enthusiast forever seeks something better or different, and is willing and anxious to pay for the newest and rarest specimens of his or her favourite flower. It is not that the real enthusiast is dissatisfied or disappointed with the older varieties, but his outlook springs rather from a very keen desire to keep in touch with the latest developments. As in other spheres, there is the natural wish to keep up-to-date and to grow or possess the best that is available. I think we can, therefore, accept the supposition that public demand for new varieties of flowers will not diminish, and from that we can also accept the probability that the interest of hybridists in the Sweet Pea is unlikely to flag.

The price of one plant of a new rose, orchid or carnation, or of a corm of a new gladiolus, alone deters many prospective purchasers during its first year of introduction; but with Sweet Peas, the cost of twenty seeds of the very latest variety does not impose a strain on even a modest purse. Incidentally, this provides yet another reason for the popularity of the flower.

Attend an exhibition of the National Sweet Pea Society and if you come to the sober conclusion that it is impossible to improve on the modern Sweet Pea, or to make the flowers more pleasing to the eye, it will not be at all surprising. Yet the same thing would have been equally true a generation back, and very appreciable changes and improvements have been effected during that period. Apart from the advent of *Countess Spencer*, change has come about so gradually that one does not quite realise the difference between the present-day

Band Aid Raised by F.C. Harriss.

Sweet Pea and Eckford's old varieties, or even the early Spencers, unless flowers or photographs of each are at hand to permit an accurate comparison.

By the end of the nineteenth century, as we have seen in the first chapter, raisers had settled down to the work of effecting minor improvements in colour or form, but none had any inkling of the drastic improvement which nature gave us in 1901. It is this completely unpredictable factor which deters me from making any hasty prophecy as to what Sweet Peas may be like twenty-five years hence. If one disregards any future generosity on the part of Mother Nature the direction of future development is still hazy enough; but, proceeding with due caution, I can venture my own firm conviction that we have by no means yet touched high water mark in the development of the Sweet Pea. We can still confidently look ahead to further improvements which will add to its beauty. In fact, the old saying, "There are more fish in the sea than ever came out of it", aptly illustrates my personal view. A few years ago I read an article in one of the horticultural trade weeklies in which the writer claimed that constant interbreeding in the case of the Sweet Pea, plus other factors, has weakened the constitution of the plant, that breeders are already at the end of their tether as far as development is concerned, and that they are in a vicious circle. He put forward the view that unless new "blood", such as crossing with another species, is introduced, there will be no advance. But I do not think we are entitled, as yet, to assume any constitutional weakening, for there is not the slightest evidence of this as far as I am aware. Further, I am quite convinced that the flower is not getting "played out". The positive evidence in the degree of improvement in some recent introductions, and in seedlings which are in existence though not yet introduced, points in exactly the opposite direction.

But let us take the flower point by point, and coldly examine and discuss those changes which are possible, probable, or desirable. Take first that most important factor, colour. At a superficial glance we might imagine that modern varieties range over almost the whole field covered by floral colours; yet we have only to consider colours and shades found in other flowers to realise that improvement in colour range alone is both possible and desirable. Compare the colours of the best of our modern varieties with, say, some of the beautiful blues found in Delphiniums, the velvety reds of Wallflowers or Roses, the clean mauve tones of some Violas, the warm, glowing, soft salmons and apricots of Gladioli, the orange tones of Begonias, the indescribable colour combinations of some Dahlias – these are all directions for colour improvement that come readily to mind. It is worth remembering that there has been no appreciable deepening in cream Sweet Peas since the time of the old Grandiflora favourite *The Hon. Mrs. Kenyon*, and I have no doubt that the elusive colour yellow will sooner or later be produced.

Apart from self colours, I am sure the possibilities with regard to bicolours, stripes, picotees, and flushes, have hardly been touched, certainly not exploited. In the past they have not greatly appealed to raisers, and apart from my own work on what are known as the *Unwin Stripes*, the varieties which have been introduced have cropped up by chance, rather than design. One can look back and very readily recall the colours of some old favourites which have no modern counterparts, colours which would be most acceptable today. I do not think distance was lending enchantment when I penned these reflections for the National Sweet Pea Society's 1947 Annual: "I would welcome with open arms a modern cerise-pink of the tone of the old *Zarina*, a true cerise like *Sincerity*, or a rich chocolate without a trace of purple, as in *Splendour*. We now have nothing possessing the silky, silvery cleanness of *Elegance*. The dainty warmth of *Audrey Crier* and *Mrs. Routzahn* is unforgettable, but here, I think, their charming tints may have been recaptured, perhaps surpassed. It is curious that the beautiful shot-silk effect of *Charles Foster* (*Agricola* was of somewhat similar character) almost completely died with that grand Pea after it had seemed to promise such wonderful possibilities to the hybridist. *Wenvoe Castle* and *Afterglow*, two old blues, also had this "shot" effect with mauve overlaying the blue in much the same way as is found in some Delphiniums. Then again, we look in vain for the clear-cut apple blossom appearance of *Eric Harvey*, or the elusive pastel tints of *Twilight*. We had several very pleasing striped and flaked Peas years ago, though *Helen Pierce* stands out in my mind with its curious veining. *The Abbott*, too, with its grey cobweb-like colouring was a great favourite of mine, though I must admit that most growers considered it freakish rather than beautiful. As a matter of fact, over the last few years there is one variety, outnumbering all others put together, which has continually been sent to my firm for identification, namely, the chocolate-striped *Fantasy*."

Yes, there is ample room for improvement in colour alone. In point of fact, the lines on which hybridists will probably work in this direction are reasonably perceptible. A potent factor which should not be overlooked is that at any time something new may appear, not necessarily startling in itself, but which will open up fresh channels to explore. Possibly "inside information" may have inspired Mr. E. R. Janes in an excellent and most interesting article entitled "The Modern Sweet Pea", which appeared in the April 1948 issue of the Journal of the Royal Horticultural Society. He wrote: "There are many signs that we are on the edge of great things – modern genetical science has advanced a long way since the days of the early Spencers." I admit that without any positive indications, I too have felt much the same kind of hopeful expectancy for the past few years. Will we, for example, ever get a buttercup yellow? I think so, but not as a mutation, more likely by crossing with another species of Lathyrus. "I cannot believe we have nearly approached the end of development", was another opinion expressed by Mr. Janes, which I most heartily endorse.

Apart from colour, suppose we now create just one Sweet Pea spike to our own specifications. How could we change its present structure to conform to our ideas and ideals of perfect beauty? What could we alter to effect improvement? *Fragrance?* Undoubtedly. *Lightness and grace?* I think not, for here the obvious effort must be to preserve what we already possess. *Size of bloom?* Yes, but with reservations. *Number of flowers on a stem?* Hardly, since most tastes are catered for already. *Shape of petals?* My imagination falters, for I cannot conceive how any alteration in this respect could possibly increase the beauty of the flower, apart perhaps from a *slightly* increased waviness, and in *some* colours, more duplex and triplex standards. I think we may profitably examine each of these points separately and in greater detail, leaving aside for the moment the equally important points of constitution, hardiness, and habit of the plant.

Until the summer of 1946 I had consistently maintained that our Sweet Peas were equal to the old type in strength of growth. This view may have been more or less correct on the score of quality, but I was undoubtedly wrong in respect to vigour. In the summer of 1946 I ran across a short row of Sweet Peas, the seed of which had come from an out-of-the-way Cambridgeshire fen village. I had no idea such Sweet Peas existed, for they were much inferior to some of my well-remembered Grandiflora favourites, such as *Prima Donna* and *Lady Grizel Hamilton.* These were obviously of pre-Eckford vintage, for their flowers were very small and short-stemmed, and even "threes" were the exception rather than the rule, whilst the few colours represented were dull and quite uninteresting. Rather surprisingly, the growth and vigour of the plants themselves were not as good as in a row of poor quality mixed Spencers growing almost alongside, a point to which I will refer later. A small bunch of these "pre-Eckford" blooms taken to my office gave rise to a good deal of amusement among the staff, for the little fellows looked just like caricatures of Sweet Peas. Their perfume gave us our biggest surprise. I realised almost immediately that this was the first time (and probably the last) that I had ever experienced the actual scent which gave our flower its name. Their scent was simply marvellous – sweet, heavy and almost overpowering. It left me in rather uneasy doubt as to whether or not I would consider it completely desirable if it could be re-introduced, but we have undoubtedly lost that great strength of perfume in modern varieties.

Many modern varieties are fragrant to greater or lesser degree, perfume being very obvious in warm, dry weather, sometimes almost absent under opposite conditions. As a rough and ready guide, I would say that the darker and more crude the colour, the more pronounced will be the scent. But there are exceptions. Possibly the old original heavy perfume would be considered somewhat sickly by some, and not as pleasant as the modern more delicate and rather elusive version. On some relative points there can be no doubt. Firstly there is the somewhat alarming fact that the coming of the Spencer type brought with it a certain loss of perfume. My 1946 experience lends colour to the surmise that this was the second distinct loss in this direction. Then again, looking back to early Spencer days, I feel

Galaxy Mixed A vigorous type with four or more blooms to a stem.

sure there has been a gradual loss of scent ever since. As a hybridist, I am convinced that the old-time perfume can and will be reclaimed, always provided there is sufficient public incentive to make the effort worthwhile. It pleases me greatly that much more interest is now taken in scent by seedsmen, raisers and the public in general, though it is still largely ignored by exhibitors.

Next we will review the factor of lightness. Obviously we cannot afford to jeopardise one of the greatest assets of the Sweet Pea. It is essentially a dainty, airy flower, as light as a beautifully coloured butterfly poised for flight. I can imagine no change of form which, if it detracts from this exquisite lightness, could possibly increase the beauty of the flower, neither can I visualise how its present grace could be enhanced.

As regards size of bloom, it is extremely unlikely that Sweet Peas with smaller, flowers than at present would be welcomed. We have every reason to expect the tendency to be quite the opposite. The exhibitor and the ordinary amateur gardener both dearly love a large flower, and it can be taken for granted that the raiser will do his utmost to meet that obvious demand. Therein, to my mind, lies a decided risk; for how far can we enlarge the Sweet Pea flower before we begin to detract from its lightness? It is very difficult to pre-determine just what may be the safe size limit before the very character of the flower is in danger. I do not think there would necessarily be any loss of beauty with a general ten to fifteen per cent increase in size of bloom, provided always that the petals have enough substance to stand up to weather conditions without protection, that the standards possess sufficient waviness to counteract or balance the increased size in respect to lightness, and that the blooms are well placed on stems which are long and strong enough to bear them. In other words, the all-round proportion has got to be exactly balanced. However, in expressing this opinion I am not wholly confident that I would personally welcome even a five per cent increase in size, and am strongly inclined to reserve final judgment until I actually see such spikes.

I am quite sure that we encounter another very real risk in seeking to increase the number of flowers on a stem. The days have gone by when the production of a majority of four-bloomed spikes was worth mentioning in a catalogue, for almost all modern kinds of Late Spencer type produce four-bloomed spikes under quite ordinary culture, whilst under the cordon system most varieties will occasionally produce five- and six-bloomed spikes in favourable conditions. Under the cordon system, well-placed fours are by no means easy to produce, whilst with fives and sixes the liability to bad placement is greatly increased. Then again, the period during which the spike is perfect is shortened in the case of fives and sixes through the greater length of time between the opening of the top and bottom flowers. Very often the bottom flower is "getting tired" before the top bloom has fully expanded. It seems to me we have almost reached the limit as far as the number of flowers on a stem is concerned in this type. And in other types we have several races of multifloras giving enough flowers per stem to satisfy most tastes. Certainly I have no wish to produce Sweet Pea spikes which, for exhibition purposes, have to be given special treatment after the method of some exhibitors of Gladiolus spikes, in order to ensure all the flowers being open at the same time. I strongly dislike any artificial methods of altering the natural character of any flower, and feel sure that immediately any such measures are adopted the average flower-lover begins to lose interest. Of course, it is quite impossible to separate the points which I have described for they are all bound up with, and inter-dependent on, each other. I might add here that I never hope to see a truly double Sweet Pea, even though, commercially speaking, it would be an undoubted financial success, at least for a short period.

There is really little I wish to add in respect to shape of the petals, for a little extra frilliness has been considered. If we could fashion our ideal flower to our liking there would be slight variations according to each one's individual taste. Perhaps my summing up may not be so far from a general or average opinion, for I would certainly not wish to alter drastically the charming outline of petal as found in the best modern varieties.

The possible lines of future improvement I have indicated do not take into account any basic structural changes in the plant itself which might result from a successful cross with other species, or indeed from a natural mutation. My personal experience is very much against the chance of obtaining anything really valuable from possible hybrids between Sweet Peas and any other species of Lathyrus. Experience also does not tend to make me favourably inclined towards freakish hybrids. Twice in the past we have raised plants which most certainly sprang from Sweet Pea seeds, but which possessed thin grass-like leaves, and flowers borne in clusters. Their petals were very narrow, not more than ⅛th inch broad, the stigma and stamens fully exposed. Neither plant produced seeds, nor would they cross-fertilise. I have come to the conclusion that these freaks were F^1 hybrids by natural cross-fertilisation with some other species. Incidentally, both originated from Californian-grown seed.

Several times in the past, quite remarkable Sweet Pea plants have appeared in our crosses or selections which have possessed appreciably greater vigour than is normal, with large, leathery foliage, broad, strong haulm, and petals approaching the thickness and texture of a rose petal. In each case the flowers possessed undeveloped stamens and a curiously misshapen and twisted pistil. Here, again, no seeds were produced and no crosses were effected.

So far, my feelings about the future have been confined to the ordinary type, but what I have said can be applied equally to the Late Spencer. Frankly, I think it unlikely that the Early Flowering Sweet Peas will ever lead this type in development or improvement. The

Supersnoop An improved Snoopea mixture. Raised by David Lemon in California.

dwarf races are a slightly different proposition. Their defects seem to arise mainly from their habit, all growth being so close to the surface of the soil.

"Several years ago a plant appeared among my father's seedlings in which the tendrils were displaced by slender, strap-like leaves. It was saved and came true to this characteristic. Hybridisation proved this characteristic to be hereditary, but, except as a curiosity, we could see no particular value in it, and did not go on with it. The stock was handed over to Professor Bateson, the well-known authority on Mendelism, then at Cambridge University. The increased 'lung-power' given by a double expanse of leaf surface might have been useful in exhibition culture where the plants are tied up and their tendrils nipped off."

The last paragraph has been "lifted" intact from the 1929 edition of this book. Since then, Mr. J. O. Tandy has introduced a new race called *Snoopea*, in which the plants produce leaves instead of tendrils, exactly the same as the earlier mutation mentioned above. This was

Lady Fairbairn Named after the President of the National Sweet Pea Society. Raised by F.C. Harriss.

followed immediately by a similar, though much-improved race called *Supersnoop*, raised by Mr. David Lemon, then with Bodgers of California. The *Supersnoops* have larger flowers, considerably longer and stronger stems, and a wider, brighter range of colours. I am sure they have come to stay.

A totally distinct type was raised fifty years ago in America – I believe by Zvolanek, which had very narrow petals. My memory may be at fault, but I think they were called *Butterfly* Sweet Peas; but I do remember that the flowers somewhat resembled the blooms of Tropaeolum Canariense. If one had never seen ordinary Sweet Peas they would have been found attractive, for their appearance was exceedingly light and dainty. But comparison was unavoidable and in consequence the type "faded out" very quickly. I made a few crosses with it but was displeased with the results. Possibly something worthwhile might have been raised if I had persevered, but at that time I did not realise the significance of taking crosses beyond the F^2 stage, or of inbreeding. From time to time one has noted pessimistic comparison between modern Sweet Peas and the old-time Grandifloras in respect to constitution, vigour, and hardiness. A few pages earlier I gave my impressions of the old pre-Eckford Grandifloras which came from the fens of Cambridgeshire. These were definitely shorter and weaker in growth than Spencers growing alongside. It seems obvious therefore that we have improved the vigour of the plant; but I am fairly sure that very little difference, if any, has taken place in its constitution or hardiness. Admittedly, many more Sweet Peas were autumn-sown in the open during Eckford's time and later, but the seed was cheaper then, and winter losses did not impose any serious financial strain. South of the Wash we seem to have forgotten that it is still reasonably safe to sow them in the open ground in the autumn – the cold frame is much more often utilised. Growers who have never sown outdoors in September or October must have noted the very great vigour of the occasional self-sown seedling which pulls through the winter without protection. Then again, comparative lack of hardiness has been blamed off-hand for the tendency of cordon-grown plants to go "blind"; but we certainly had occasional blind plants fifty years or more ago, and we did not then sow quite as early as we do today, nor did we check the plants in mid-winter by transplanting – factors which I think might logically contribute more largely to blindness than any real or fancied constitutional weakness. A good deal more evidence must be produced before I begin to get apprehensive that Sweet Peas are getting constitutionally weaker. Even "streak", which at one time seemed to threaten the very future of the flower, is not met with as frequently now as in the time of the early Spencers. It is easier to accuse the Sweet Pea of getting "soft" than to pin the trouble on changed cultural methods; but I feel sure that if we force the pace by somewhat unnatural methods, an occasional adverse reaction should not be unexpected. If the Sweet Pea was propagated by means of cuttings, graftings or division, one would give greater credence to any suspicion of constitutional deterioration; but it is raised from seeds, and through the steady influx of new varieties raised by cross-fertilisation, hybrid constitutional vigour is maintained to a greater degree than with many similar species.

In any attempt to look ahead there is yet one other factor which must be taken into account, namely the effect on progress and development of the specialist societies. Since 1900 the organisation which has wielded the greatest influence on the destiny of the Sweet Pea is the National Sweet Pea Society of this country. Its membership is numbered in the thousands, but this bears little relationship to the Society's importance and influence, or indeed to the popularity of the flower whose interests it serves. The advantages the Society offers its members are out of all proportion to the annual subscription, and it has always puzzled me why many more Sweet Pea lovers do not claim these advantages. Practically every Sweet Pea grower of note in this country, whether trader or amateur, has been associated with the N.S.P.S. The trade perhaps used to overshadow and outbalance amateur influence in the past; but of late years amateurs have taken a greater responsibility for the Society's management, and never to my knowledge has there been a more congenial atmosphere in the conduct of its affairs. It would be an exceedingly difficult task to enumerate all those famous Sweet Pea personalities who have, from the first, contributed to making the N.S.P.S. one of the most respected and influential specialist societies of our time. However, it is impossible to describe this Society without mentioning some of its officers, and first of all, the President, Lady Fairbairn, who has held that office now for a number of years. No wonder exhibitors respect and even love her! She grows and exhibits as they do, is invariably bright and cheerful, with a friendly word for one and all, very like our beloved Queen Mother. Then there is the late Chairman of Committee, T. C. Baines, who gave many years of valuable work, and who has been replaced by his deputy chairman, that great enthusiast W. G. Maishman. The Hon. Treasurer, E. J. Pratt, efficiently makes sure the Society keeps in first class financial shape and is responsible for putting some novel ideas for raising money into working order. J. R. F. Bishop is Editor of the Annual, and since he took over this job it has become increasingly interesting and helpful. T. B. Sewell, helped I believe by his wife, has taken over the Bulletin from Bernard Jones, and here I hope more space will be given to the ordinary Sweet Pea lover as distinct from the exhibitor. Last, but by no means least, mention must be made of the Hon. Secretary, L. H. O. Williams, who, to my mind, is the most efficient and helpful of a long line of good Secretaries. Nothing seems too much trouble for him, as readers will find out if they have occasion to write to him. In all fairness I ought not to overlook the members of the General Committee, but there is not enough space to write about every one of them. Yet I feel I must mention two – both of them very old friends of mine – Len Everitt and Bernard Jones who, for year after year, have brought wise and commonsense contributions to Committee meetings. I strongly

Our Joyce A variety with good weather resistance.

advise every lover of the Sweet Pea to join the Society and to give his or her support to an organisation which has done, and is doing, so much for the flower.

It is very easy for a specialist society to give undue emphasis to the exhibitor's interests and point of view, or to permit trade interests to distort its influence. The exhibitor's flower is not necessarily the ideal for the man in the street, and the undue exploitation of purely exhibition points might conceivably change the very character of a flower and make it less valuable from the ordinary amateur's point of view. Fortunately for the Sweet Pea the N.S.P.S. has always maintained a reasonable balance in all phases of its activities. The manner in which its exhibitions are held is irreproachable, and the encouragement given to beginners is an excellent example which some other specialist societies might copy with advantage. The Sweet Pea Annual, published by the Society, is by any standard worth more than the total yearly subscription; but in addition, its other publications, though mainly of a cultural nature, are invaluable. The sponsoring of Trials of new varieties inevitably carries with it the liability for criticism, since few individual raisers and other enthusiasts will ever entirely agree with the decisions of any committee which judges Trials. Looking back over the work of the various committees which have adjudicated at the N.S.P.S. Trials, it is easy to find instances of a really good seedling being passed over, but not nearly as easy to find varieties which have been given awards and which later have proved quite unworthy.

Midnight The finest dark maroon variety.

Up to 1947 the rules made it possible for raisers who had seedlings at the N.S.P.S. Trials to be elected to the adjudication committee (Floral Committee). Thus it often happened that some members of this committee were actually helping to judge their own introductions. This state of affairs, though rather surprising, is not by any means uncommon in the realm of horticulture. The strongest argument in favour of such a seemingly risky arrangement has always been that there are not enough efficient judges if the services of "interested" experts are dispensed with. There are many, including myself, who have never admitted the accuracy of this claim. I have always felt that it is more logical to claim that a committee composed entirely of raisers is less likely to reflect public taste and requirements than a committee of ordinary enthusiasts. Most other specialist societies are also confronted with this same problem.

As far back as I can remember, the inclusion of "interested" judges has always been a cause of dissatisfaction within the membership of the N.S.P.S. Sometimes it has smouldered for a period, and on occasion it has flamed up into acrimonious controversy. A number of notable Sweet Pea enthusiasts, including my father, objected strongly to the old system years ago, and, after an unsuccessful attempt to get the rules altered, I am afraid most of them allowed their interest in the Trials to wane. Opposition to the old well-tried method was usually interpreted by its upholders as a direct imputation of "fiddling", if not of deliberate cheating, which of course did nothing to improve matters. Unfortunately, too, discussions, both in private and in public, tended to become personal and narrow in scope, rather than being based on the broad impersonal question of the principle involved.

The last time the whole thing came to a head was at the Annual General Meeting of 1946 when a motion by the Rev. D. Gourlay Thomas sought to debar any person from judging who had a seedling at the Trials that year. As the motion was circulated to all members before the Meeting this was well attended and very representative. To quote the official report: "It was the occasion of a debate as distinguished as it was dignified, that would not have disgraced the highest chamber in the land." In describing the actual debate the report went on: "The Rev. Gourlay Thomas handled his case well. Speaking with moderation, he dismissed . . . any suggestions of deliberate dishonesty in the past on the part of our judges, but he argued that it was scarcely humanly possible for a judge to be disinterested regarding a seedling of which he thought so highly as to send it to trial. He rebutted any suggestion that the talent necessary for judging was not obtainable from disinterested parties." Then came some well-reasoned and weighty arguments against the motion from A. W. Gower, Charles H. Curtis and A. J. Macself, men who rightly deserved the confidence of all members and with many years of experience to influence their opinions. They claimed that the standard of judging would suffer under the proposed new rule, and that only raisers possessed the knowledge to determine with accuracy whether a Novelty was really an improvement on existing varieties. These three speakers left no doubt in the minds of their listeners as to the serious nature of the decision which was to be taken. An opportunity of voicing my own convictions came and I think that my arguments served to allay the fears of many members that the new proposal was not a practical one. The fact that I was a trader, a raiser, and had served on the Floral Committee, gave point to my contentions, and this was not overlooked by those present. After further discussion, an amendment from J. McGregor, which provided a compromise, was defeated, but a further amendment (accepted by the Rev. Gourlay Thomas), extending the scope of the original motion, was carried by a substantial majority, and the new rule read: "No person shall be a judge of the Sweet Pea Trials who has, or whose firm, company, or employer, have a seedling that year at the Trials". It will give readers a very good idea of the admirable spirit permeating the N.S.P.S. if I quote a further extract from the official report: "The debate was remarkable for the restraint of all parties and by the absence of any feeling of rancour, a Meeting which was not only highly creditable to the Society but was enjoyed by all."

This decision should be considered in the light of a protracted trial, a step in the right direction, but not necessarily the end of a journey. In any case it certainly set a standard which might profitably be examined by similar organisations. My personal view is that efficiency could be still further improved. I have never believed that Sweet Pea Trials could ever be as accurately judged at one visit as is possible with two, or even three, visits at intervals of ten or fourteen days. To my mind also it is quite essential that every member of the Floral Committee should know Sweet Peas really well. To be a good judge of flowers in general does not provide the necessary qualification. There should, moreover, always be a reasonable range of the best standard varieties available for comparison during judging, providing these are given exactly the same cultural treatment as the seedlings on trial. At present one feels that the number of standard varieties available for comparison at the Trials is always quite inadequate. Then, again, at the final judging, cut blooms which have been at least twenty-four hours in water would provide the ultimate indication of real merit. We should never lose sight of the fact that the value of the flower is largely bound up with its cut bloom qualities. Each judge should, off his or her own bat, record an individual estimate of value by means of a points system. I distrust the show of hands method which is so often preceded by "guiding" comments from one or more forceful personalities. An attempt to sway the meeting might be legitimate and even desirable in debate, but in judging the value of a new Sweet Pea I do think it important that personal inclination should be allowed the fullest scope, unhampered by any "prompting". If judges did not object to their individual pointing being made public, so much the better in the long run, for this would prove of great help at the next election of the Committee.

Some raisers do not regularly send all their new seedlings to any Trials, and there are also other reasons why a good new Sweet Pea sometimes fails to get official recognition. I see no great objection to permission being given to the N.S.P.S. General Committee to demand the inclusion of any named variety once, under number, in order to verify its qualities. Such a concession would considerably minimise the chance of a really good Sweet Pea completely escaping recognition. It would admittedly be a case of "better late than never". All these are purely personal suggestions which, in my opinion, would make the

Frances Perry Improved A sunproof, vigorous variety.
Raised by Charles Unwin.

judging of Sweet Pea Trials more accurate, more water-tight, and more valuable.

The N.S.P.S. continues to do all that it possibly can to further the best interests of the flower, and it deserves every support. Many local Horticultural Societies are affiliated to the N.S.P.S., and they, under the benevolent guidance of the N.S.P.S., are contributing their share to the welfare of the flower. There are also other great organisations such as the Scottish National Sweet Pea, Rose and Carnation Society, whose influence one must not overlook. This Scottish Society has for many years sponsored its own Sweet Pea Trials, and it is quite safe to add that the results of these Trials have furnished a pretty accurate guide to the amateur grower of the comparative merit of the new varieties submitted by most of the well-known raisers, at home and abroad.

Thus we see that the future of the flower is being fostered and guided by individuals and organisations who can be depended upon to spare no efforts on its behalf. It only remains for me to add the personal conviction that, although the Sweet Pea has had a wonderful past, a yet more glorious future lies ahead, always provided that men and women keep loving their flowers, and as long as this crazy world is not ruined by atom bombs, or worse.

INDEX